Contracts for Independent Readers

Adventure

Grades 4–6

Writers:
Dee Benson, Colleen Dabney, Rusty Fischer, Michael Foster, Frankie Germany,
Beth Gress, Terry Healy, Kimberly Minafo, Lori Sammartino

Editors:
Kim T. Griswell and Cayce Guiliano

Contributing Editors:
Deborah T. Kalwat, Scott Lyons, Diane F. McGraw

Art Coordinator:
Donna K. Teal

Artists:
Nick Greenwood, Sheila Krill, Mary Lester,
Greg D. Rieves, Rebecca Saunders, Donna K. Teal

Cover Artist:
Nick Greenwood

www.themailbox.com

Manufactured in the United States

10 9 8 7 6 5 4 3 2 1

Table of Contents

About This Book

What is adventure?

Adventure novels include exciting action and danger as the key elements. The conflict is almost always between man and nature but can involve cunning villains against daring heroes. Often the reader is left asking, "What will happen next?" rather than "Why?" or "To whom?"

How to use this book:

Contracts for Independent Readers—Adventure includes everything you will need to implement an independent reading program in your classroom.

The **Teacher's Organizational Checklist** on page 4 will help you monitor your students' progress throughout the year. To use this page, photocopy it to make a class supply and write each student's name in the space provided. Hold a conference with each student to assess the goals the student has for the semester or the year. Have the student write her goals in the space provided. Next, have each student choose one of the novels included in this book to read. List the title of the book in the appropriate column. When the student has completed an activity, write the date it was completed in the bottom portion of the corresponding box. Use the key at the bottom of the page to note the type of activity completed in the top portion of the corresponding box as shown in the sample. After evaluating the activities, write any comments you have in the space provided and have the student do the same. At the end of the semester or year, direct each student to complete the self-assessment portion detailing how she feels she has done at reaching her goals. Finally, write your own assessment of each student's progress.

The **introductory page** of each independent contract contains a description of the novel, background information on the author, and a student contract materials list. This list will aid you in preparing in advance any materials that students may need. Most of the listed materials can be found right in the classroom!

Each of the two programmable **contract pages** in each unit has six independent activities for students to choose from. Each unit also includes **reproducible pages** that correspond to several independent activities. The second contract page has slightly more advanced activities than the first contract page.

Since some novels are at higher reading levels or may contain more mature content, we suggest that you read each of the novels so that you may assist students in choosing which novels to read.

Also included in this book is a **student booklist** on page 61, which consists of 12 adventure novels, with a brief description of each. This list provides you with additional titles for students who finish early, for students who would enjoy reading other books in this genre, and for you to include in your classroom library.

Other Books in the Contracts for Independent Readers Series:
- *Contracts for Independent Readers—Historical Fiction*
- *Contracts for Independent Readers—Humor*
- *Contracts for Independent Readers—Realistic Fiction*
- *Contracts for Independent Readers—Fantasy*
- *Contracts for Independent Readers—Mystery*

Name _____

4

Book Title	Activity 1	Activity 2	Activity 3	Activity 4	Activity 5	Activity 6	Activity 7	Activity 8	Activity 9	Activity 10	Activity 11	Activity 12	Teacher Comments	Student Comments
Sample: Book Title	MA 11/6	SS 11/7			LA 11/10									

Student Goals:

Self-Assessment:

Teacher Assessment:

Key

LA = Language Arts
RD = Reading
W = Writing
MA = Math
SS = Social Studies
SC = Science
A = Art
MU = Music
RS = Research
CT = Critical Thinking

Call It Courage
by Armstrong Sperry

About the Book

Mafatu, a Polynesian boy, nearly drowns in a storm that takes his mother's life. Since then, he has been terrified of the sea. He is taunted by his peers and ashamed. He believes his father, the Great Chief of Hikueru, is also ashamed of him. To try to conquer his fears and make his father proud, Mafatu, Uri (his dog), and Kivi (the albatross) set out to sea on a heroic journey. They survive days of nature's cruelty and at last find themselves beached on a strange island. Mafatu struggles against nature, his own fears, and cannibals. He escapes the island with the cannibals in pursuit but also with a secure claim to courage. Mafatu returns home to his joyous father. Today, the people of Hikueru still sing of Mafatu's bravery and how he came to deserve his name—Stout Heart.

About the Author

Armstrong Sperry (1897–1976) was born in New Haven, Connecticut. He loved to draw and listen to the tales told by his great-grandfather, a seafaring man. He loved exciting adventures that took place in the most remote parts of the world.

Sperry's training at the Yale Art School was interrupted by World War I when he enlisted in the navy. After the war, he studied art in New York and Paris. Then he worked in advertising, but in the back of his mind he felt the lure of the South Seas. He sailed on a schooner to the island of Bora Bora. In 1925, Sperry joined a museum expedition as an ethnologist and sailed again in the South Pacific, learning the languages, the legends, and the music of the islands. He drew pictures and stored up memories, many of which have found their way into his books for young readers.

Student Contract Materials List

- Activity #1: paper, pencil
- Activity #2: copy of page 8, dictionary, crayons or markers, scissors, 18 index cards, glue, hole puncher, string
- Activity #3: 1 sheet of white paper, colored pencils or crayons
- Activity #4: copy of page 9, scissors, yarn or string, crayons, hole puncher, construction paper, coat hanger
- Activity #5: 4 sheets of graph paper, reference materials on sea creatures
- Activity #6: 3 sheets of white paper; scissors; glue; colored pencils, crayons, or markers
- Activity #7: blank cassette tape, tape recorder, drum or rhythm instrument
- Activity #8: paper, pencil
- Activity #9: copy of page 10, twelve 3" x 5" index cards, markers or crayons, 1 die, 2 game tokens
- Activity #10: 24" x 24" piece of cardboard, newspaper, wheat paste or liquid starch, large bowl, tempera paint, arts-and-crafts supplies
- Activity #11: paper, pencil
- Activity #12: reference materials on the South Pacific, arts-and-crafts supplies, science project display board, crayons or markers

Call It Courage
Independent Contract

Name: _____ Number of activities to be completed: _____

 1. **Writing**

Mafatu leaves home in the dark of night when he feels he can no longer tolerate the shame of his fear. He doesn't tell anyone that he is leaving. Pretend that you are Mafatu and write a letter to your father so he will not worry about you. Explain why you are leaving and what you hope to do. Try to help him understand your need to make this journey on your own.

 2. **Social Studies**

Mafatu's adventure takes him to a remote volcanic island with many different land and water characteristics. Obtain a copy of page 8 from your teacher and learn more about these characteristics as you make a picture dictionary.

 3. **Language Arts**

Extreme adventure vacations are in high demand by many thrill seekers today. Make a flyer advertising a vacation cruise to Mafatu's Island. Tell about all the exciting things a person may do while there, such as riding the giant lava slides, observing marine life, taking canoe-carving classes, and more. Include colorful artwork to excite vacationers about the once-in-a-lifetime experience of Mafatu's Island.

 4. **Social Studies**

Mafatu leaves Hikueru in a hurry, packing almost no supplies for the journey. When the storm throws him up on the island beach, he has no water, food, clothing, shelter, or tools to help him survive. Obtain a copy of page 9 from your teacher and create a necessity mobile.

 5. **Science**

Create a crossword puzzle with the words below. First, use graph paper to plan how the words will cross each other. On another sheet of graph paper, draw your completed crossword puzzle. Number each word in the first letter's space. Then research each sea creature to write the clues for your puzzle. Below the puzzle squares, write the clues in numerical order under the headings "Across" and "Down." Make two copies: one for a key and one for a friend to solve.

dolphin	whale	flying fish	manta
jellyfish	eel	coral	tiger shark
clam	sand shark	parrot fish	squid

 6. **Language Arts**

Mafatu had several victories over his fears. Make a comic strip of the major events of his courageous adventure. Cut three sheets of white paper in half lengthwise. Glue them end to end to form one long strip. Mark the strip to form 12 equal sections. On a separate sheet of paper, list the main events of the story beginning with Mafatu's decision to leave home. Then, in sequential order, draw a comic strip illustration for each event on each section of your strip, ending with Mafatu's joyous return home. Under each illustration, write a caption explaining what is happening.

Call It Courage

Independent Contract

Name:_____ Number of activities to be completed: _____

7. Music

Pretend you are the storyteller of Mafatu's island village. Write a song or chant to go along with a familiar tune (or compose an original song) about Mafatu's journey and his great courage. Use a drum or rhythm instrument to accompany your voice. Record your musical story on a cassette tape and share it with the class.

8. Writing

Pretend that you are Uri, Mafatu's faithful dog. From the dog's point of view, write the story you would tell the other dogs in the village about three of the events on the island. Consider how Uri may have viewed the events differently from Mafatu. For example, Uri may tell the other dogs that he jumped into the water with the shark to force Mafatu to face his fear and fight the shark.

9. Language Arts

Complete a board game of Mafatu's journey. First, obtain a copy of the gameboard on page 10 from your teacher. Add details to the gameboard, such as a shark or the cannibals' war canoe. Then make a set of 12 cards for the game by writing an event from the story on each card, along with instructions on where the player is to move. For example, "You slide down the lava flow. Move forward three spaces" or "Your coconuts wash overboard. Move back one space." Use a die to play the game with a friend. The first player to complete Mafatu's journey is the winner!

10. Social Studies

Reread chapter 3 to find specific facts about the landforms, places, and vegetation of the island. Then make a three-dimensional map of the island. Use papier-maché to shape the landforms. When the map dries, paint the land and water. Use other arts-and-crafts supplies, such as pipe cleaners and pasta pieces, to add details such as the jungle and lava slide. Include a legend or map key to explain the details of your map.

11. Critical Thinking

Kivi, the albatross, and Mafatu were both picked on by others. Mafatu understood Kivi and helped him. As the story progresses, Kivi often comes just in the nick of time to help Mafatu. A proverb says "A friend in need is a friend indeed." Do you think this is true? Write a short essay to explain why or why not. In your essay, give examples from the book and from your own experience.

12. Research

Armstrong Sperry traveled all around the South Pacific on a museum expedition. Research one island, or chain of islands, in the South Pacific. Gather or make models of objects—such as seashells, tropical plants, animals, musical instruments, etc.—to use in creating a mini museum exhibit. Use a science project board to display information and illustrations about the items and the island. Then share your mini museum exhibit with the class.

Picture Dictionary

Use a dictionary to find the definition of each word below. Write each definition in the corresponding box. Cut the boxes apart and glue each one on a separate index card. On the back of each card, illustrate the word. Next, choose at least five additional words from the story related to the land or sea that are unfamiliar to you. Write each word on a separate index card and then define and illustrate each word. Title and illustrate a blank index card to make a cover for your picture dictionary. Punch a hole in the upper left-hand corner of each card. Stack all of the cards in alphabetical order with the cover on top. Finally, use a piece of string to tie the cards together.

1. atoll	2. foothill
3. island	4. islet
5. beach	6. lagoon
7. mountain	8. plateau
9. barrier reef	10. sea
11. valley	12. volcano

Note to the teacher: Use with activity #2 on page 6.

Necessity Is the Mother of Invention

Mafatu finds himself on a deserted island with no water, food, clothing, shelter, tools, or weapons for protection. In order to survive, he must provide himself with the basic needs written on the shapes below. First, lightly color and cut out each shape. Then use your book to find ways Mafatu meets each need. Write your findings on the back of the shape. Punch a hole where indicated on each shape and tie varying lengths of yarn or string from each hole. Tie each shape to a coat hanger and add a construction paper title as shown in the diagram.

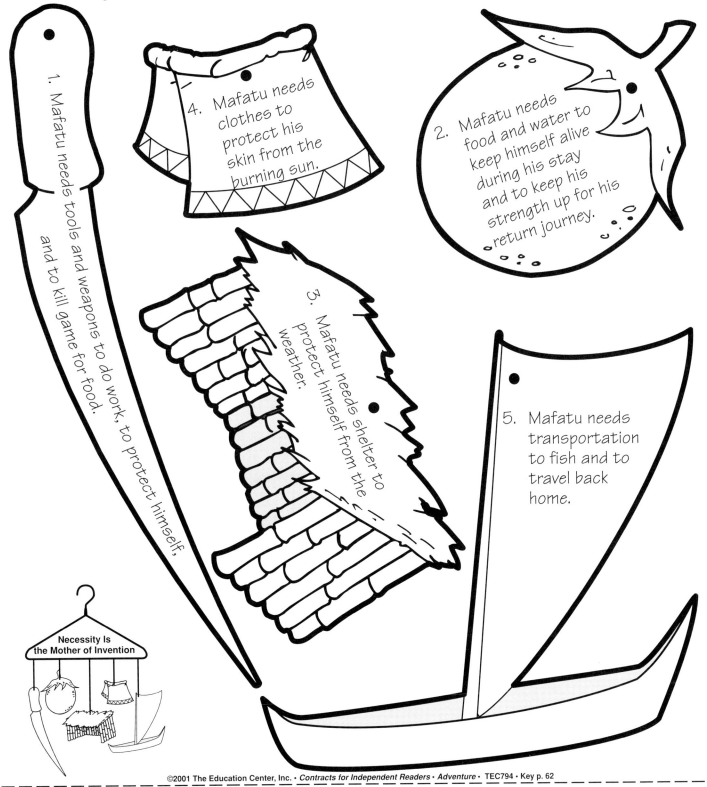

1. Mafatu needs tools and weapons to do work, to protect himself, and to kill game for food.

4. Mafatu needs clothes to protect his skin from the burning sun.

2. Mafatu needs food and water to keep himself alive during his stay and to keep his strength up for his return journey.

3. Mafatu needs shelter to protect himself from the weather.

5. Mafatu needs transportation to fish and to travel back home.

Necessity Is the Mother of Invention

Note to the teacher: Use with activity #4 on page 6.

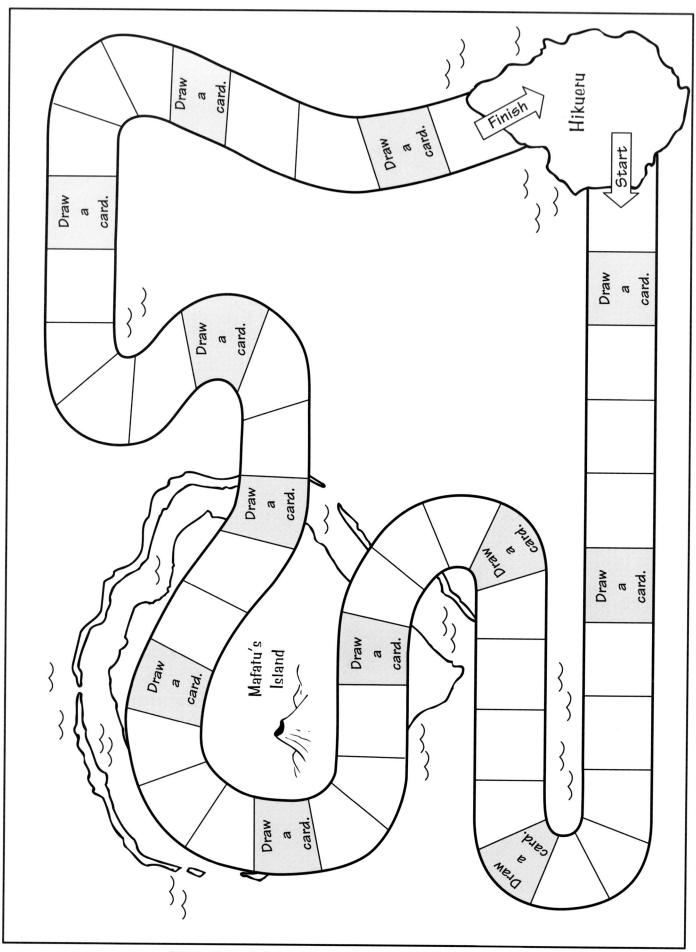

Note to the teacher: Use with activity #9 on page 7.

The Cay
by Theodore Taylor

About the Book

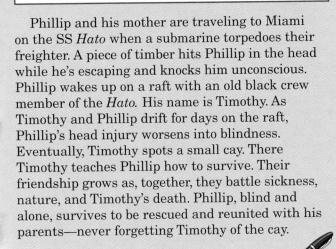

Phillip and his mother are traveling to Miami on the SS *Hato* when a submarine torpedoes their freighter. A piece of timber hits Phillip in the head while he's escaping and knocks him unconscious. Phillip wakes up on a raft with an old black crew member of the *Hato*. His name is Timothy. As Timothy and Phillip drift for days on the raft, Phillip's head injury worsens into blindness. Eventually, Timothy spots a small cay. There Timothy teaches Phillip how to survive. Their friendship grows as, together, they battle sickness, nature, and Timothy's death. Phillip, blind and alone, survives to be rescued and reunited with his parents—never forgetting Timothy of the cay.

About the Author

Theodore Taylor was born on June 23, 1921, in North Carolina. Theodore was raised during the Great Depression and wrote sports stories for a Virginia newspaper at age 13. When he graduated from high school, he became a copyboy for the *Washington Daily News* in Washington, DC. Working for the newspaper developed his writing skills, but he always regretted not going to college.

At 21, Taylor joined the merchant marines and the naval reserve. He grew to love naval history, which gave him the background for books such as *The Battle off Midway Island*. Background for *The Cay* came from his experiences while stationed in the Caribbean, where he provided hurricane relief. Phillip Enright is based on someone Taylor knew as a child.

After leaving the navy, Taylor became a press agent for a Hollywood film production company. He quickly advanced to story editor and assistant to the producer. Later Taylor left the glamour of Hollywood for the realism of documentary films. With numerous awards and over 30 books to his credit, Taylor continues writing seven days a week from his home office in California—except during football season.

Student Contract Materials List

- Activity #1: copy of page 14
- Activity #2: crayons or markers, hole puncher, yarn, 5 sheets of white paper
- Activity #3: access to the library or Internet
- Activity #4: copy of page 15
- Activity #5: crayons or markers, ½ sheet of poster board, acccss to the Internet
- Activity #6: crayons or markers, glue, 2 craft sticks, 2 paper plates, yarn
- Activity #7: glue, scissors, two 2" x 3" sheets of different-colored construction paper, one 3½" x 5" sheet of light-colored construction paper

- Activity #8: research materials on coconuts and seed dispersal
- Activity #9: reusable materials, such as pieces of cork, sponge, and wood; glue
- Activity #10: reference materials on the Caribbean, crayons or markers, ½ sheet of poster board
- Activity #11: copy of page 16, reference materials on sharks, crayons or colored pencils
- Activity #12: crayons or markers, 15 index cards, index card box, reference materials on tropical sea creatures

The Cay
Independent Contract

Name:_____ Number of activities to be completed: _____

 1. ### Social Studies

Chapters 1 and 2 tell about Phillip and his parents. In chapter 4 Timothy tells about himself and his family. How much could you tell about your family? Obtain a copy of page 14 from your teacher and ask family members to help you fill in your family tree. Share your family tree with the class.

 2. ### Writing

Pretend you are Phillip, writing journal entries to tell your friend Henrik van Boven about your experiences on the cay. On five separate sheets of paper, write one paragraph per page, using the prompts below to help you get started. Then illustrate your entries. Bind your pages together using a hole puncher and yarn.

- An important lesson I learned is…
- The best thing about the cay is…
- I was frightened when…
- The food was…
- The animals were…

 3. ### Music

Timothy hums and sings calypso in *The Cay*. This island music originated on Trinidad in the Caribbean Sea. Improvising lyrics is very important in calypso; many singers make up rhymes on the spot. Go to the library and obtain a copy of "The Banana Boat Song (Day-O)" or find the lyrics online. Then make up your own words to the song. Ask your classmates to join you in singing your version of this popular song.

 4. ### Reading

Timothy and Phillip face many conflicts in *The Cay*. Obtain a copy of page 15 from your teacher and list some of the different challenges they face.

 5. ### Research

Timothy takes safety precautions prior to the hurricane that hits the cay. Would you know what to do in a hurricane? Contact your local weather station or use the Internet to find information on how to stay safe during a hurricane. Then, using this information, design a public service poster outlining the steps you should take to prepare for a hurricane.

 6. ### Art

Timothy and Phillip have some differences but also share many similarities. Use two paper plates, crayons or markers, and yarn to make the faces of these characters. On the back of each plate, list at least five character qualities for each person, some of which may be listed on both plates. Attach a craft stick handle to the bottom of each plate. Then use the faces to act out a scene from the story.

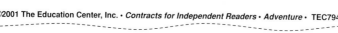

The Cay

Independent Contract

Name:_____ Number of activities to be completed: _____

 7. | **Art**

As Phillip weaves palm branches together into sleeping mats, the cay weaves Phillip and Timothy together as friends. Obtain a 2" x 3" rectangle from two different colors of construction paper. Choose one of the two-inch ends of each rectangle as the top and trim the edges to round them. Cut about four equal slits in each rectangle, from the bottom to one-fourth inch from the rounded top. Weave the two pieces together to make a heart. Glue the heart to a 3½" x 5" sheet of construction paper to make a friendship card. Personalize your card with a quote about friendship and give it to a special friend.

 8. | **Science**

Timothy feels that he is too old to climb, so he wants Phillip to climb the coconut palm trees to get coconuts for them. Timothy longs to taste the milk and meat of this tropical fruit. How do you think the coconut palm trees got on the cay? Research coconuts and seed dispersal to find out how this wonderful tree probably found itself on an out-of-the-way cay. Then write a story as if you were a coconut, using your research to tell about your travels and how you helped Phillip and Timothy on the cay.

 9. | **Critical Thinking**

When Phillip explores the island after the hurricane, he finds no use for items blown ashore, such as pieces of cork and sponge. Gather similar reusable materials from home and school to construct a model raft or boat. Place your vessel in water to make sure it floats. Then give your seaworthy vessel a name.

 10. | **Writing**

The Cay shows what life was like in the Caribbean during World War II. Today, tourism is big business in the Caribbean. Use travel books, magazines, brochures, and the Internet to find information about the Caribbean. Then write a script for a television commercial advertising an island in the Caribbean. Along with your script, include a poster that describes the island and highlights the attractions of that island.

 11. | **Science**

After Phillip stumbles off the raft into the water, Timothy yells, "I tol' you 'bout d'shark!" What do you know about sharks? Obtain a copy of page 16 from your teacher and test your knowledge about these amazing fish.

 12. | **Research**

The sea creatures listed below are mentioned in The Cay. Research these interesting animals. Next, write each animal's name on the front of an index card. On the back of each corresponding card, draw a picture of the animal and write several facts about it. Then use reference materials on Caribbean sea animals to make five additional sea creature cards. Store your cards in an index card box to create a Caribbean sea creature fact file.

langosta	mussels	scallops	parrot fish
pompano	sea urchins	eels	
sharks	skates	barracuda	

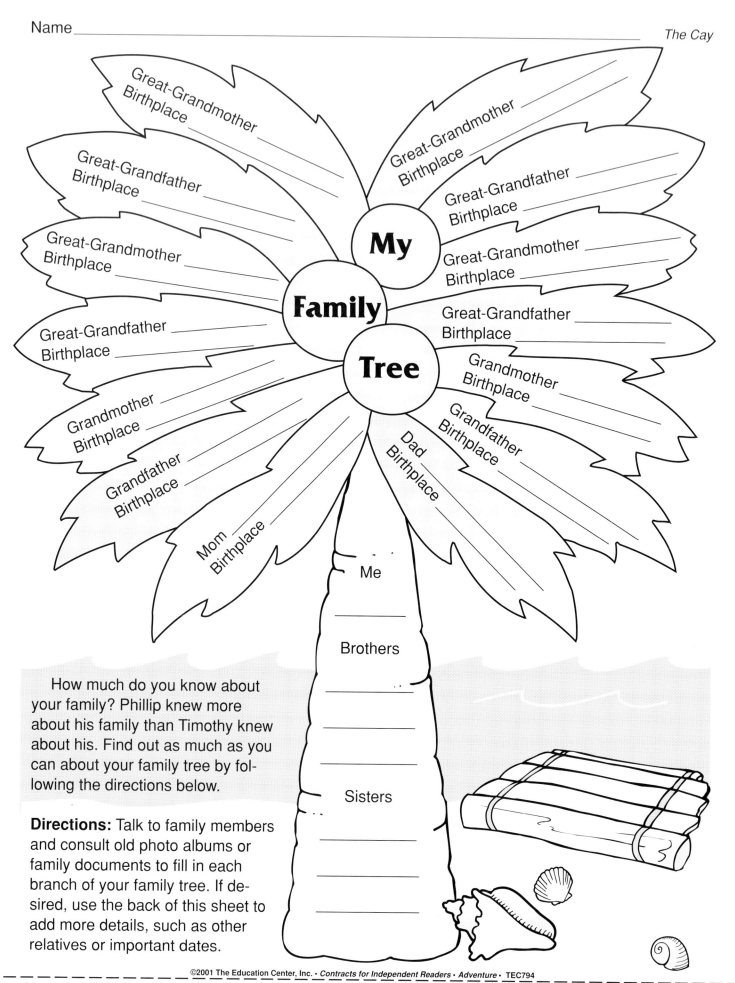

Great-Grandmother
Birthplace _____

Great-Grandmother
Birthplace _____

Great-Grandfather
Birthplace _____

Great-Grandfather
Birthplace _____

Great-Grandmother
Birthplace _____

My

Great-Grandmother
Birthplace _____

Family

Great-Grandfather
Birthplace _____

Great-Grandfather
Birthplace _____

Tree

Grandmother
Birthplace _____

Grandmother
Birthplace _____

Grandfather
Birthplace _____

Grandfather
Birthplace _____

Dad
Birthplace _____

Mom _____
Birthplace _____

Me
_____

Brothers
_____
_____

Sisters
_____
_____
_____

How much do you know about your family? Phillip knew more about his family than Timothy knew about his. Find out as much as you can about your family tree by following the directions below.

Directions: Talk to family members and consult old photo albums or family documents to fill in each branch of your family tree. If desired, use the back of this sheet to add more details, such as other relatives or important dates.

©2001 The Education Center, Inc. • *Contracts for Independent Readers • Adventure •* TEC794

14   **Note to the teacher:** Use with activity #1 on page 12.

Cracking Conflict

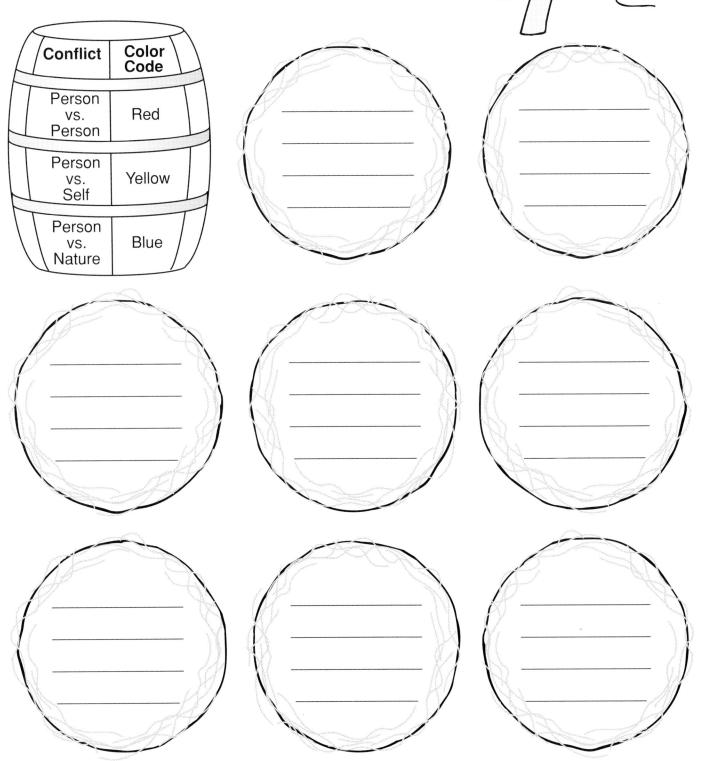

Conflict is the problem in a story that triggers action. Look back through *The Cay* and find important conflicts that Phillip and Timothy face. Write each conflict on a coconut below. Decide which kind of conflict is experienced, and then lightly color the coconut according to the code. Make sure you have at least one example of each type of conflict listed.

Conflict	Color Code
Person vs. Person	Red
Person vs. Self	Yellow
Person vs. Nature	Blue

Note to the teacher: Use with activity #4 on page 12.

Shark Smart!

From the moment that Phillip ends up on the raft with Timothy, the two of them are surrounded by sharks. There are sharks in the water around the raft and sharks in the water around the cay. Follow the directions below to separate the true shark statements from the false shark statements.

Part I Directions: Read the statements about sharks below. Decide if each statement is true or false. Use reference materials for help, if needed. Color in the correct answer.

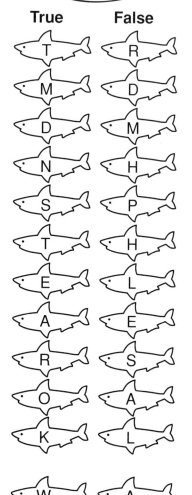

True   **False**

1. Sharks can't replace their teeth.

2. Sharks, rays, and skates all belong to the same class of fish.

3. Most sharks are not dangerous to people.

4. Scientists classify about 100 species of sharks.

5. Sharks have the same five senses that humans do.

6. The spiny dogfish shark is the world's largest fish.

7. Most sharks give birth to live young.

8. Baby sharks are called cubs.

9. Sharks use an electrosense for navigation and finding prey.

10. All sharks are herbivores.

11. The movie *Jaws* featured a mechanical great white shark and was directed by Steven Spielberg.

12. Sharks often die of cancer.

13. A person who studies sharks is called a stenographer.

14. White sharks rank among the most dangerous sharks.

15. A shark has no bones in its body.

Part II Directions: Unscramble the colored letters to find the name of an unusual shark that is sometimes found in tropical seas. Wrtie your answer in the blanks below.

___ ___ ___ ___ ___ ___ ___ ___   ___ ___ ___ ___ ___

Dogsong
by Gary Paulsen

About the Book

In this novel for mature readers, Russel Susskit, a young Inuit (sometimes known as Eskimo) teen, yearns to learn more about his heritage and about the "old way" of Inuit life. Living as a modern-day Inuit, Russel feels an emptiness inside. Hungering to become more, he leaves home to live with Oogruk, the old shaman, who teaches Russel how to live the old way. Soon, Russel is ready to lead Oogruk's dogs, the last remaining dogsled team in his village, on a journey northward. It is a long journey, requiring great physical, emotional, and spiritual strength. As Russel and his team of dogs forge northward into the Arctic, he learns what it means to survive in the wilderness, to grow into manhood, and to become one with his dogs and with the earth.

About the Author

Gary Paulsen was born on May 17, 1939, in Minneapolis, Minnesota. His father was a career Army officer, so Gary lived with his mother in Chicago, where she worked in a munitions plant. At age seven Gary and his mother went to the Philippines to be reunited with his father. Moving constantly, Gary had trouble in school. One day a librarian offered him a library card, and to Gary, this was like being handed the world. He began reading science fiction, westerns, and the classics.

Paulsen worked in maximum-security, high-tech jobs for the government until he decided to quit and become a writer. He enjoys dogsledding and has twice competed in the Iditarod dogsled race across Alaska. Besides fiction and nonfiction books for young readers and adults, Paulsen has written plays and a screenplay. He has won many honors for his books, including the Newbery Honor citation, the Children's Book of the Year Award, and the Parents' Choice Award.

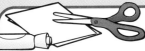

Student Contract Materials List

- Activity #1: box, newsprint, five 3" x 5" index cards, crayons or markers, arts-and-crafts supplies
- Activity #2: copy of page 20
- Activity #3: cassette tape, tape recorder
- Activity #4: light-colored construction paper, crayons, 10" length of yarn, scissors, hole puncher
- Activity #5: 12" x 18" light-colored construction paper, reference materials on Alaskan camping, crayons or markers
- Activity #6: 3 sheets of 9" x 9" white paper, scissors

- Activity #7: copy of page 21
- Activity #8: reference materials on the Inuit; $\frac{1}{2}$ sheet of poster board; crayons, markers, or colored pencils; map of Alaska and northern Canada
- Activity #9: reference materials on Arctic wildlife, shoebox, arts-and-crafts supplies, index card
- Activity #10: paper, pencil
- Activity #11: file folder, old magazines, scissors, glue, crayons or markers
- Activity #12: reference materials on the Arctic; $\frac{1}{2}$ sheet of poster board; crayons, markers, or colored pencils; scissors

Dogsong

Independent Contract

Name:_____ Number of activities to be completed: _____

 1. Social Studies

Create a time capsule that could have been made by Russel Susskit. Collect arts-and-crafts supplies with which to make items showing the old way of Inuit life. For example, you could use clay to make a model of an oil lamp like the one Russel finds in chapter 8 or use pipe cleaners to fashion a dogsled as described in chapter 3. Make at least five items. Then write a few sentences about each one on an index card. Finally, cover a box with newsprint, decorate it with scenes of Inuit life, and store your items in it.

 2. Reading

By the story's end, Russel undergoes a personal transformation, leaving behind modern boyish ways and becoming an Inuit man of the old way. Obtain a copy of page 20 from your teacher and think about several of the significant changes Russel undergoes on the journey to find his Dogsong.

 3. Language Arts

In part I, Oogruk tells Russel stories of the old way of life. Storytelling is an Inuit tradition in which the elders teach children the old ways and what is expected of Inuit men and women. Make plans to talk with an older relative, neighbor, or friend. Begin by scheduling a convenient time to meet. Then write six to eight interview questions. (For example: How did you spend afterschool time? What was the most interesting thing you did as a child?) Use a tape recorder to record your interview and any stories that arise in your conversation. Share your recording with the class.

 4. Language Arts

Gary Paulsen uses many specialized words from Inuit life, such as *muktuk* and *gangline*. Use the book to find 15 vocabulary words related to Russel's life and their definitions. On construction paper, trace around your hand to make a mitten shape and cut it out. Use it as a pattern to make 15 additional mittens. On the front of each mitten, write and illustrate one word. On the back, write the definition. Hole-punch each mitten shape in the cuff area. Thread the mittens onto a ten-inch length of yarn with the title-page mitten on top. Tie the yarn to secure the pages.

5. Research

Gary Paulsen conceived the idea of *Dogsong* when he was camping in Alaska. Late at night, surrounded by his sleeping dogs, he wrote with a headlamp shining on his notebook. Use reference materials to gather facts on camping in Alaska. Which Alaskan parks have campgrounds? What kind of specialized gear would a camper need for a week in the Alaskan wilderness? Fold a piece of construction paper into thirds and organize the information as an illustrated pamphlet. Include helpful hints Russel might give a first-time wilderness camper.

 6. Writing

Cold, fear, and the beauty of nature are three recurring themes in *Dogsong*. Use sensory words and the steps below to write a cinquain poem on each of the three themes.

Line 1—two syllables (the subject)
Line 2—four syllables (describing the subject)
Line 3—six syllables (showing action)
Line 4—eight syllables (expressing feeling)
Line 5—two syllables (describing or renaming the subject)

Center each poem in the middle of a nine-inch circle of white paper. Fold the circle in half several times and cut the edges to form a snowflake, being careful not to cut your poem.

Dogsong

Independent Contract

Name:_____ Number of activities to be completed: _____

7. Reading

The old shaman Oogruk teaches Russel a great deal about the old way of Inuit life. Obtain a copy of page 21 and use it to document the many lessons Russel learns.

8. Research

The Arctic is a challenging place to live. The largest group of native North American Arctic peoples—the Inuit—are sometimes known as Eskimos or "eaters of raw meat," but they prefer to be called Inuit, which means "the people." Research this tribe to gather information about the old and the modern ways of these Arctic residents. Trace a large map of Alaska and northern Canada. Shade the areas where the Inuit live. Around the border of your map, draw pictures and write about important aspects of their lives, including housing, clothing, food, language, travel, and art.

9. Science

Select one Arctic animal, such as the caribou or polar bear, and research its physical characteristics, habitat, and eating habits. Use a shoebox and arts-and-crafts supplies to construct a diorama showing the animal in its natural environment. On an index card, write a paragraph about the animal and then attach the card to the back of the diorama.

10. Writing

At the end of part 3, Russel and the dogs bring Nancy to the edge of the land. They follow the snowmobile trail toward the setting sun and the village they know is near. Then the author leaves the reader to decide what happens next. Take over the job of author and tell the rest of the story. First, consider how Russel has grown and how Nancy changes his life. Does he decide to continue his long journey, or does he decide to stay in the village, realizing that people need people? Write an ending that brings the story to a logical conclusion.

11. Art

Russel's journey leads him far along the path toward his goal for knowledge and personal fulfillment. Think about a goal you have for your future. What path must you follow to reach it? What challenges might you encounter in the quest for your dream? On the inside of a file folder, make a collage of cutout or drawn pictures and words representing your vision of life's journey. Russel's song is titled "Dogsong." Write your name and the title of your song on the front of the folder.

12. Social Studies

Research the Arctic region. Construct a large flip book by folding a sheet of poster board in half and using a pencil to divide the top fold into four equal sections. Cut along the pencil lines to form four flip-up pages. Do not cut past the fold. Label the bottom edge of each flip-up page with one of these topics: "Geography," "Climate," "Vegetation," and "Wildlife." Then illustrate each labeled page. Under each flip-up page, write a factual paragraph about its topic. Share your Arctic region book with the class.

Russel Transformed

Russel undergoes a major transformation in the course of *Dogsong*. Document five changes in Russel and his life in the spaces below. On the left-hand side, write details about Russel when he lives at home. On the right-hand side, write the corresponding change that occurs as a result of his stay with Oogruk and his long journey.

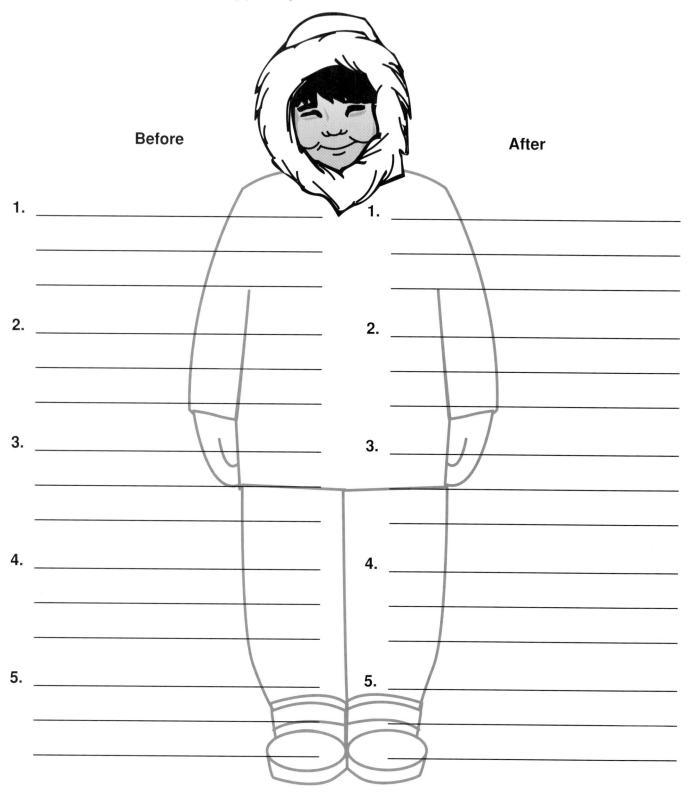

Before

After

1. _____
_____
_____

2. _____
_____
_____

3. _____
_____
_____

4. _____
_____
_____

5. _____
_____
_____

1. _____
_____
_____

2. _____
_____
_____

3. _____
_____
_____

4. _____
_____
_____

5. _____
_____
_____

Note to the teacher: Use with activity #2 on page 18.

Lessons Learned

Oogruk teaches Russel many lessons about the old way of Inuit life, lessons he knows Russel will need to remember on his long journey north. For each chapter listed below, write one lesson Russel learns in that chapter. On the back of this sheet, write five of the most important lessons you have learned in your lifetime.

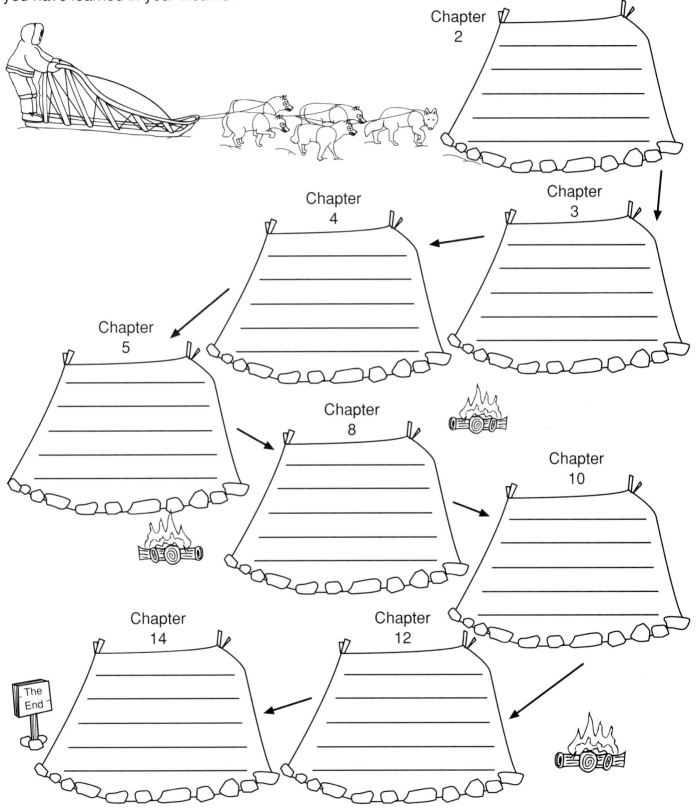

Note to the teacher: Use with activity #7 on page 19.

Baby Island

by Carol Ryrie Brink

About the Book

Mary and Jean Wallace are cast off to sea in a lifeboat when the steamship they are on begins to sink. With them are 20-month-old twins, a four-month-old baby, and a one-year-old toddler! When they reach a deserted island, they begin to look for fresh water. Once they find a stream, they begin to explore the island further and make some of the things they will need, such as a tepee to sleep in, dishes, and a playpen for the babies. They soon realize that they are not alone on the island. Through many trials and adventures, the girls manage to take care of themselves and the babies until help arrives and they are rescued.

About the Author

Carol Ryrie Brink was born on December 28, 1895, in Moscow, Idaho, and was orphaned at an early age. She grew up in the care of her aunt and grandmother, who were wonderful storytellers. Carol always wanted to be a writer. Her most famous book, *Caddie Woodlawn,* is based on a story she heard often of her grandmother Caddie's Wisconsin childhood.

Carol attended the University of Idaho and received a bachelor of arts degree from the University of California Berkeley in 1918. She later married Raymond Brink, a mathematician. She published her first book in 1934 and eventually wrote more than 30 fiction and nonfiction books for children and adults as well as several plays. She received the Newbery Award in 1936 for *Caddie Woodlawn*. In 1965, Carol was awarded an honorary doctorate of literature from the University of Idaho. She died in 1981.

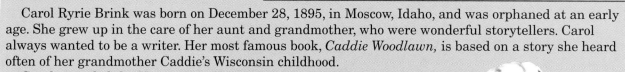

Student Contract Materials List

- Activity #1: craft sticks, toothpicks, or other craft supplies; white paper; scissors; glue; crayons
- Activity #2: map of the Pacific Ocean, reference materials on Pacific islands, 12" square of light-colored construction paper, scissors, glue, construction paper
- Activity #3: 10" fabric square, clay, string, sticks
- Activity #4: eight 3" x 5" index cards, crayons or colored pencils, permanent black marker, construction paper
- Activity #5: paper, pencil
- Activity #6: copy of page 25, scissors, crayons or colored pencils

- Activity #7: reference materials on state and provincial flags, 12" x 18" white fabric, fabric paints or permanent markers
- Activity #8: copy of page 26
- Activity #9: reference materials on Sir William Wallace, ½ sheet of poster board, scissors, crayons or markers, glue
- Activity #10: paper, pencil
- Activity #11: fresh whole coconut, recipe book, cooking items required for recipe
- Activity #12: ½ sheet of poster board; glue; fine-tipped markers; natural items such as sand, twigs, rocks, and shells

Baby Island

Independent Contract

Name: _____ Number of activities to be completed: _____

1. **Art**

Jean discovers a secret compartment in the boat while looking for milk for the babies. Use craft sticks, toothpicks, or other craft supplies to make a model of the lifeboat. Include the secret compartment, the items the girls find in the boat, and other details described in chapter 2. Then make paper cutouts of the girls and the babies. Use the boat and paper cutouts to act out one of the scenes from the book.

2. **Social Studies**

The *Orminta* becomes disabled in the Pacific Ocean. Using a map of the Pacific, trace a path with your finger from San Francisco to Australia. Research one island your finger crosses and create a triarama. Fold a 12-inch square of construction paper in half to form a triangle. Unfold and refold the paper so that the opposite corners touch. Unfold the paper again and cut along one fold line to the center. Overlap and glue the two bottom triangles. Then use the information you gathered to create an island scene, adding three-dimensional elements to complete your triarama.

3. **Art**

The girls build a tepee and a stockade (play-pen). Make a model of one of these items using only the supplies listed below. Reread the portions of chapters 6 and 7 that describe these items to make sure that your model has the same features. Then share your model with the class.

10" fabric square   clay   string
sticks

4. **Writing**

While they are stranded on Baby Island, Jean manages to write to her aunt a few times. She sends her letters floating on the Pacific Ocean in empty cans. Use index cards to make eight postcards. On the front of each card, illustrate an important event in the girls' adventure, such as building the tepee by the waterfall. On the back of each card, write a message to Aunt Emma about the event. Then make a can by cutting two can shapes, larger than the index cards, out of construction paper. Tape the side and bottom edges, leaving the top open. Place your postcards inside the can.

5. **Music**

Jean likes to make up silly songs to sing when she is happy. Reread some of her songs in chapters 5, 7, 12, and 13. Notice how she uses rhythm and rhyming words to make her songs flow. Think about some of the things that make you happy. Then make up a silly song of your own about one of these things. Remember to make it rhyme. Finally, sing your song for the class.

6. **Language Arts**

In this tale of adventure, Carol Ryrie Brink challenges the reader with some interesting new words. Obtain a copy of page 25 from your teacher and take on the challenge of solving a vocabulary puzzle.

Baby Island
Independent Contract

Name: _____ Number of activities to be completed: _____

7. Art

When the girls at last discover the stream of fresh water, Jean makes a flag of her blue handkerchief and claims the island for the president of the United States and themselves. Design your own flag for Baby Island. First, research various state and provincial flags for the meanings of colors and symbols used on flags. Then plan a detailed emblem, choosing colors and other design elements that match the Baby Island adventure. Finally, following your plan, use fabric and fabric paints or markers to make the new flag of Baby Island.

8. Science

Mary learns firsthand the realities of the ocean's tides which she had previously only encountered in her school textbooks. Obtain a copy of page 26 from your teacher and learn more about the ocean's tides.

9. Social Studies

Mary and Jean Wallace refer to William Wallace numerous times and even sing a Scottish song about him to remind themselves to be brave. Research Sir William Wallace. Then draw an outline of a coat of arms and divide it into four sections. On each of the four sections, illustrate a different fact about his life; then cut out the coat of arms. Write an informative paragraph about the Scottish hero, glue it to the back of your shield, and share it with the class.

10. Writing

Among the items Mary finds in her pocket is a small notebook with a calendar in the back. She records the names and ages of each of the six castaways in it. Pretend to be Mary and write one day's entry in your notebook diary. Choose a day that is especially eventful for the island adventurers. Tell the details of the day and also of Mary's feelings of delight, fear, and longing that she expresses only in her diary.

11. Science

Baby Island provides plenty of food for the castaways, from bananas to gull eggs. The coconut is one delightful treat that puts them in good spirits. They eat it right out of the shell, cooked in pudding, and baked in a banana coconut pie. Find a coconut dessert recipe you might like. Then have an adult help you crack open a fresh coconut. Save the milk and peel off the husk. Prepare the recipe for your class to sample. Share the sweet leftover coconut meat and milk, too!

12. Social Studies

When Jean first finds large human footprints on the beach, she thinks they belong to *Robinson Crusoe*'s Friday or to a pirate. Fortunately, they belong to a grumpy Englishman, Mr. Peterkin. Even so, the chest of gold doubloons he found proves there were once pirates on the island. Sketch a treasure map of Baby Island. Include and label places mentioned in the book and choose a spot for the chest of gold to be buried. Then add natural items—such as sand, twigs, rocks, and shells—to make your map three-dimensional.

©2001 The Education Center, Inc. • *Contracts for Independent Readers • Adventure • TEC794*

Puzzling Vocabulary

The jigsaw puzzle below contains six interesting words from *Baby Island.* Choose six additional words and write them on the remaining numbered puzzle pieces. Then, on the pieces that match each numbered word, write the corresponding definition. On the back of the puzzle, lightly draw and color your favorite scene from the book. Cut out the puzzle pieces and enjoy the challenge of reconstructing it.

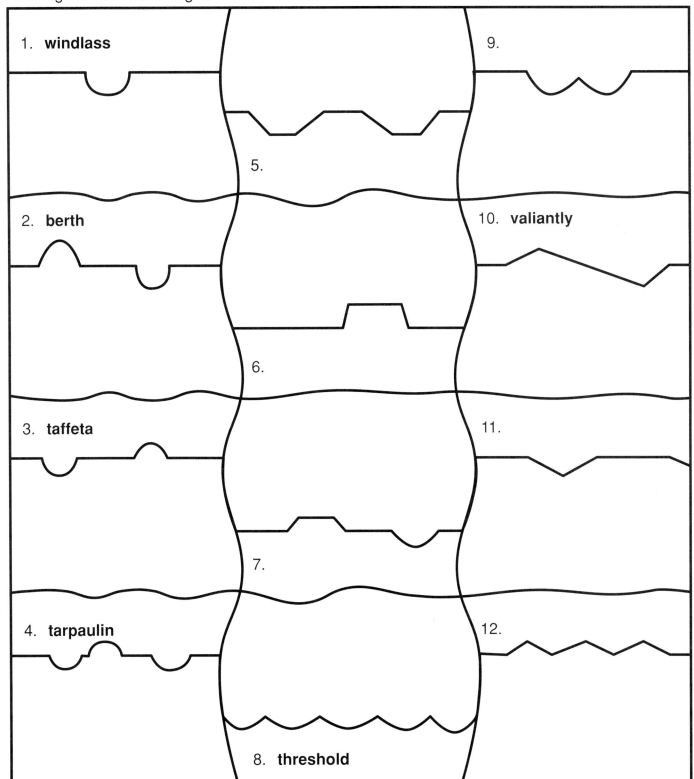

1. **windlass**

9.

5.

2. **berth**

10. **valiantly**

6.

3. **taffeta**

11.

7.

4. **tarpaulin**

12.

8. **threshold**

Time and Tide Wait for No One

The ocean's tides are caused mainly by the moon's gravitational pull on the earth. Read about high and low tides below. Use the information to complete the tide charts. Then use the tide charts to help Baby Island's residents plan their activities for the four days shown on the charts.

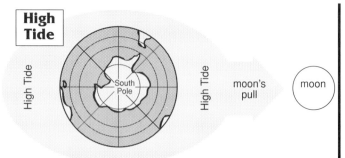

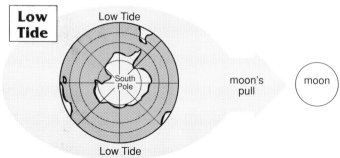

High tide occurs directly below the moon and at the same time on the opposite side of the earth. The illustration above shows the South Pacific at high tide. Its next high tide will be about 12 hours and 25 minutes later when the earth's rotation moves the South Pacific opposite the moon.

As the earth turns on its axis, the tide gradually falls until it is low tide as shown above. Low tide occurs on opposite sides of the earth halfway between the two high tides. Low tides are also about 12 hours and 25 minutes apart.

Mon.	Tues.	Wed.	Thurs.
5:00 A.M.			7:30 A.M.
5:25 P.M.	6:15 P.M.	7:05 P.M.	

Mon.	Tues.	Wed.	Thurs.
11:13 A.M.		12:53 P.M.	1:43 P.M.
11:38 P.M.	12:28 A.M.		

1. Mary and Jean went to the cave on Wednesday evening, but it was high tide and they couldn't enter. What time is best for them to return on Thursday to explore the cave? _____

2. Low tide is the time to dig for clams on the beach. What is the best time for Mary to go clamming on Monday? _____

3. If Mr. Peterkin wants to fish at high tide every afternoon this week, how much later will he go fishing on Thursday than on Wednesday? _____

4. How much time passes between Monday's first high tide and Tuesday's first high tide? _____

5. If you were to visit Baby Island and wanted to dig for clams, what times would you choose to go on Monday, Tuesday, Wednesday, and Thursday? Why?

_____

_____

_____

6. Write your own word problem in the space provided using the two charts above.

_____

_____

_____

_____

_____

Hatchet
by Gary Paulsen

About the Book

Thirteen-year-old Brian Robeson is on his way to spend the summer with his father in Canada. As the small plane in which he is flying glides over the uninhabited wilderness, the pilot suffers a fatal heart attack. After the plane crashes into a lake, Brian swims to shore with just the clothes on his back and one valuable tool—his hatchet. For the next 54 days, Brian learns the skills he needs to be able to hunt for food and protect himself against porcupines, mosquitoes, moose, and tornadoes. Through his ordeals, Brian becomes a new person—confident, resourceful, and thoughtful.

About the Author

Gary Paulsen was born on May 17, 1939, in Minneapolis, Minnesota. Gary's father was a career Army officer, so Gary lived with his mother in Chicago, where she worked in a munitions plant. At age seven Gary went with his mother to the Philippines to be reunited with his father. Moving constantly, Gary had trouble in school. One day a librarian offered him a library card. To Gary, this was like being handed the world. He began reading science fiction, westerns, and the classics.

As an adult, Paulsen worked in maximum-security, high-tech jobs for the government until he decided to quit and become a writer. Paulsen enjoys dogsledding and has twice competed in the Iditarod dogsled race across Alaska. Besides fiction and nonfiction books for young readers and adults, Paulsen has written plays and a screenplay. Paulsen has won many honors for his books, including the Newbery Honor Award, the Children's Book of the Year Award, and the Parents' Choice Award.

Student Contract Materials List

- Activity #1: 1 long stick, white paper, ruler, scissors, tape
- Activity #2: clay, white paper, clock or watch, pencil
- Activity #3: 8½" x 14" white paper, crayons or markers
- Activity #4: paper, pencil
- Activity #5: blank cassette tape, tape recorder
- Activity #6: copy of page 30

- Activity #7: reference materials on Canadian plants, 11 index cards, crayons or markers, piece of yarn, hole puncher
- Activity #8: paper, pencil
- Activity #9: copy of page 31
- Activity #10: copy of page 32
- Activity #11: healthy snacks (broccoli, pretzel sticks, vegetable dip, etc.), paper plate
- Activity #12: white paper, crayons or markers

Hatchet

Independent Contract

Name:_____ Number of activities to be completed: _____

 1. | **Reading**

Brian marks the passage of time by his successes, such as First Meat Day, First Rabbit Day, and First Arrow Day. Make a calendar of events for *Hatchet.* Obtain a long stick (at least two feet long). Then cut twenty 1" x 4" strips of paper. Write a different major event from each chapter, including the epilogue, on each strip. Tape each strip to the stick about an inch or so apart. When you are finished, the stick will be your calendar of events!

 2. | **Math**

Brian relies on the position of the sun to tell time. Make a sundial to find out how accurate they are. Place a small piece of clay on the eraser end of a pencil. Stand the pencil upright in the middle of a sheet of paper so the clay will hold the pencil in place. Place your sundial near a sunny window. At each hour, mark where the shadow of the pencil is cast and label the mark with the hour. Continue marking the hours as long as the sun shines in the window. For the next week, examine your sundial each day. How accurate is it? What are some of the disadvantages of using a sundial?

 3. | **Critical Thinking**

Brian is lost in the wilderness with only the items in his pockets, what he is wearing, and his hatchet. Imagine that you are lost in a deserted setting with only the contents of your desk. First, take an inventory of the contents of your desk. Then fold a sheet of paper in half several times to make the same number of boxes as you have items in your desk. In each box, write the name of the item and then draw a picture to show how you could use that item in a survival situation.

 4. | **Writing**

Brian does a good job of surviving alone, using his hatchet and his own mental resources. Imagine that you are stranded in a deserted place. Where do you think you would best be able to survive? In the mountains? On an island? Think about how you would survive, what you would eat, where you would sleep, etc. Then write a plot summary for a movie about your adventure. Include the actor who would play you, the setting, any problems you would face, and your daring rescue.

 5. | **Language Arts**

Gary Paulsen wrote a sequel to *Hatchet* called *The River.* In this book, a young *psychologist* (a doctor who studies the human mind) convinces Brian to take him back to the wilderness and show him how he survived. Imagine that you are the psychologist interviewing Brian about his experience. Write a list of at least ten questions to ask Brian. Then write the answers to the questions as you imagine Brian would answer them. Tape-record your interview using different voices for Brian and the psychologist. Share your interview with the class.

 6. | **Language Arts**

Characters in a story usually have some type of conflict to overcome. Three types of conflict are *person vs. person, person vs. nature,* and *person vs. self.* Obtain a copy of page 30 from your teacher and find out what types of conflicts Brian faces.

Hatchet

Independent Contract

Name: _____ Number of activities to be completed: _____

 7.

Science

Create a "Survivor's Guide to the Canadian Wilderness" that Brian would have found useful. Research at least ten edible, nonpoisonous, and useful plants that can be found in the Canadian wilderness. On separate index cards, draw a picture of each plant. On the back of the corresponding card, write the name of the plant and several facts you learned about it that would help Brian survive. On a separate card, design a cover by writing the title and your name. Finally, punch a hole in the left-hand corner of each card and tie the cards together with a piece of yarn.

 8.

Critical Thinking

Brian encounters many problems before and after the plane crash. Some of these he can solve on his own, but some are beyond his control. Make a chart with three columns labeled "Brian's Problem," "Brian's Solution," "Other/No Solution." In the first column, brainstorm a list of at least ten problems Brian encounters. Then, for each problem, decide if Brian can solve it. If he can, write his solution or possible solution in the second column. If Brian can't solve the problem or if he needs help solving it, write that information in the last column.

 9.

Math

Other than his hatchet, Brian has no supplies. Pretend that you are planning to spend three months in the wilderness. Unlike Brian, you have $500 to spend on equipment and supplies. What will you buy? Obtain a copy of page 31 from your teacher and complete it as directed.

 10.

Language Arts

Brian has many character traits that enable him to survive, such as patience and tenacity. What other traits would be necessary to survive an experience like Brian's? Obtain a copy of page 32 from your teacher and find out.

 11.

Social Studies

Brian learns the layout of his environment so that he can find food and not get lost. Reread chapters 4 and 6, in which the author describes the lake and its surroundings. Sketch the layout of the lake and surrounding area on a paper plate. Then create a map, using healthy snacks to represent the different natural features. For example, you could use broccoli for trees, pretzels for sticks, vegetable dip for the lake, etc. Include a legend showing what each snack represents. Finally, share your map with the class.

 12.

Art

Gary Paulsen wrote another book about Brian titled *Brian's Winter*. In this book, Brian is not rescued right away and is forced to stay in the wilderness through the winter. Think about all the things that Brian will have to face with the coming of winter. Fold a sheet of paper into six squares. Unfold the paper and in each square draw a picture showing Brian in the winter facing several different challenges, such as finding food, keeping warm, and staying away from hungry animals.

Conflicts in the Canadian Wilderness

Brian faces many conflicts in *Hatchet*. The main conflict in the book is Brian's struggle against nature. He also has conflicts with himself and other characters. Complete each shape below with events from the book that demonstrate each type of conflict.

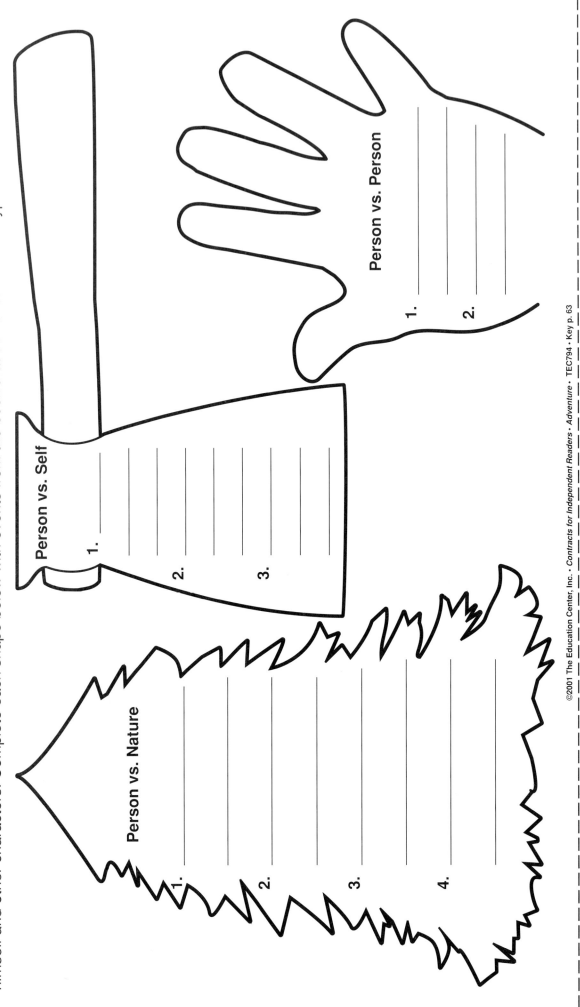

Person vs. Self

1. _____
2. _____
3. _____

Person vs. Person

1. _____
2. _____

Person vs. Nature

1. _____
2. _____
3. _____
4. _____

Note to the teacher: Use with activity #6 on page 28.

Survival on a Budget

Imagine that you are going to spend three summer months in the wilderness and you have been given $500 to spend on equipment and supplies. Look through several cata- logs to find what you will need. Then follow the directions below to complete the chart.

Directions: Write the item you want to buy in the first column, what it will be used for in the second column, and its price in the third column. Then subtract the price of each item from the previous total in the fourth column and list the amount you have left in the last column. If you need additional space, continue the chart on the back of this sheet.

Remember that you only have $500 to spend. The first item has been chosen for you.

Item	Use	Price	Subtract From Amount Left	Amount Left
flashlight	gives light	$6.00	$500.00 – $6.00	$494.00
			$494.00 –	

1. Imagine that instead of $500, you are only allowed to spend $400. What would you eliminate from your list? _____

2. Imagine that the $400 you were given is cut in half. What else would you eliminate from your list? _____

3. Would your list change if you were going to be stranded in the winter as opposed to the summer? Why or why not? _____

_____

Survival Pack

Part I Directions: What qualities do you think you would need in order to survive in the wilderness? For each quality below, write how it would help you survive.

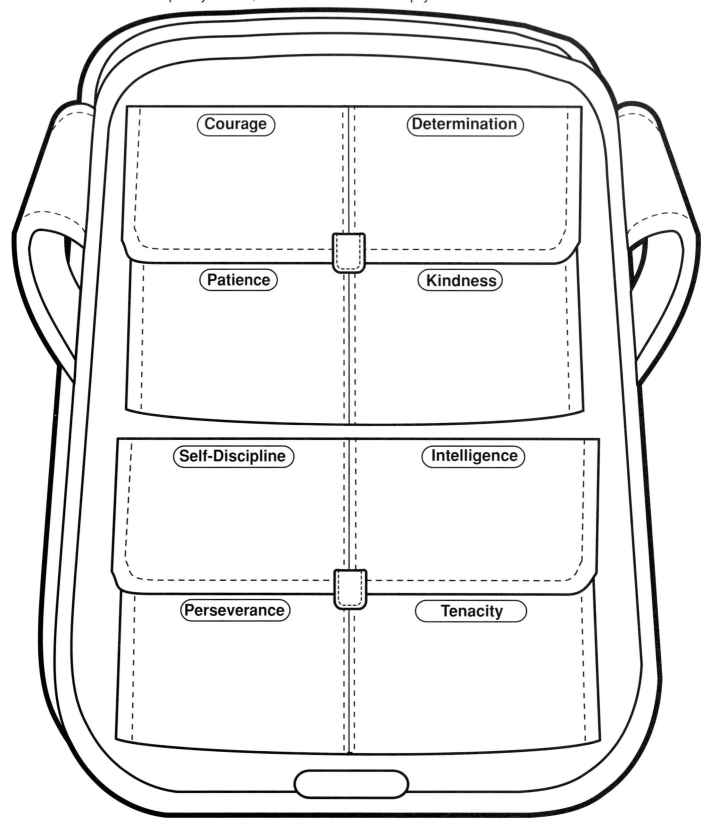

Courage

Determination

Patience

Kindness

Self-Discipline

Intelligence

Perseverance

Tenacity

Part II Directions: Highlight the qualities that you feel you already have.

Island of the Blue Dolphins
by Scott O'Dell

About the Book

Karana and her family live on a small island off the southwestern coast of California. When trouble breaks out between Aleut otter hunters from the far north and the men in Karana's tribe, many are killed. Haunted by the memories of their slain loved ones, Karana's people decide to leave the Island of the Blue Dolphins. As they leave, Karana realizes that her younger brother, Ramo, is not on the ship. She jumps into the churning sea and swims back to the island and her brother. Soon afterward, Ramo is killed and Karana must find the courage to survive alone. With a remarkable understanding of her environment, an ability to use available resources, and a deep respect for the animals that share her world, Karana lives alone on the island for many years as she awaits rescue.

About the Author

Scott O'Dell was born in Los Angeles, California, on May 23, 1898. His father worked for the railroad, so the family moved often but not very great distances. One home was on Rattlesnake Island where the water washed up under the stilts that supported their house.

O'Dell attended Occidental College, the University of Wisconsin, and Stanford University. He was not interested in learning all that was required of him. He took the courses that most interested him and did not worry about graduation. After college O'Dell held many jobs, including Hollywood camera man. *Island of the Blue Dolphins* was his first novel for young adults. He claimed that he didn't truly write for children; he wrote for himself, and his experiences come through in his writings. When writing, O'Dell worked every day of the week from 7 A.M. to noon. He received the Newbery medal for *Island of the Blue Dolphins*. Scott O'Dell died in 1989.

Student Contract Materials List

- Activity #1: white paper, crayons or colored pencils
- Activity #2: reference materials on earthquakes, crayons or colored pencils, copy of a U.S. map
- Activity #3: copy of page 36, crayons or colored pencils
- Activity #4: reference materials on animals, two 12" x 18" sheets of light-colored construction paper, scissors, yarn, coat hanger, crayons or markers, ruler, hole puncher
- Activity #5: round balloon, 9" x 12" sheet of light-colored construction paper, scissors, glue, markers, ruler
- Activity #6: copy of page 37, crayons or markers
- Activity #7: 9" x 12" sheet of light-colored construction paper, colored pencils
- Activity #8: construction paper, crayons or markers
- Activity #9: reference materials on explorers of the Channel Islands, white paper
- Activity #10: two 9" x 12" sheets of light-colored construction paper, two 4" x 6" sheets of red construction paper, scissors, glue, black marker
- Activity #11: crayons or markers
- Activity #12: copy of page 38

Island of the Blue Dolphins

Independent Contract

Name:_____ Number of activities to be completed: _____

1. Language Arts

Imagine a vacation trip to a modern resort on Karana's warm, tropical island. Feel the refreshing breeze blowing over you as you bask in the sun on the Coral Cove beach at the exclusive Blue Dolphins Vacation Resort. Create an illustrated brochure advertising a week's vacation on the island. Include descriptive words and phrases that would entice someone to visit the island. What exciting activities, such as swimming with dolphins or hunting abalone, does the resort offer to its visitors?

2. Science

The Island of the Blue Dolphins lies just off the coast of California, where earthquake activity is common. Research the cause of earthquakes and the areas of the United States that are at risk for earthquakes. Find out about safety procedures during and after earthquakes. Create a map of the United States. Color the map to show the regions of high, middle, and low potential earthquake danger. Include a key or legend for your map. On the back of your map, write a short summary explaining the cause of earthquakes and listing suggestions for safety procedures during and after earthquakes.

3. Social Studies

Scott O'Dell describes the Island of the Blue Dolphins through Karana's eyes in great detail. Reread the descriptions of the island in chapter 2 and in other places throughout the book. Think about the places Karana lives, hunts, and gathers supplies. Then obtain a copy of page 36 from your teacher and follow the directions to complete the activity.

4. Research

Animals provide Karana with food, protection, materials for tools, and companionship. Research four animals mentioned in the book. Then draw and cut out 12 four-inch circles. Write an animal name on each of four circles. On the back of each circle, write five facts about that animal. On four other circles, draw pictures of the four animals. Then, on the last four circles, describe at least one use that Karana has for each animal. Hole-punch the tops and the bottoms of each circle. Using yarn, string together the circles for each animal. Then tie them to a coat hanger to create a mobile of the animals that help Karana survive.

5. Art

Karana struggles for more than a year to spear the giant devilfish, or octopus. Reread the description of the devilfish in chapters 16 and 19 and follow the steps below to create your own devilfish.

1. Inflate and tie a balloon.
2. Cut out eight 1" x 9" strips of construction paper.
3. On each strip, write a phrase from the book that describes the devilfish.
4. Glue the strips around the center of the balloon.
5. Add facial features with paper scraps or markers.

6. Language Arts

The Island of the Blue Dolphins is filled with figurative language, which adds beauty and detail to create visual images. Obtain a copy of page 37 from your teacher and take the challenge of painting your own word pictures using similes and metaphors.

Island of the Blue Dolphins

Independent Contract

Name: _____   Number of activities to be completed: _____

Art

In the author's note, the real Karana leaves the island and is only able to communicate her story through signs because no one speaks her language. Imagine that the only way you can communicate Karana's story is through *pictographs*, or picture writing. Draw a series of pictures telling about one of the events below. Then challenge someone who has not read the book to interpret your story.
- departure of the tribe leaving Karana and Ramo stranded
- taming of Rontu
- Karana's friendship with Tutok
- Karana's rescue from the island

Writing

Imagine that you are the real Karana returning to the Island of the Blue Dolphins after living at the mission for ten years. Write a *cinquain*, expressing your thoughts and feelings about the 18 years you spent alone on the island. Use the pattern below to create your cinquain. When your poem is complete, copy and illustrate it on a sheet of construction paper.
- Line 1: Two syllables announcing the topic
- Line 2: Four syllables describing the topic
- Line 3: Six syllables expressing action
- Line 4: Eight syllables expressing feeling
- Line 5: Two syllables giving a synonym for the topic

Research

Did Aleuts, Russians, and people from other countries really visit the island home of Karana's people? Research to learn more about the exploration of the Channel Islands. List the countries whose people visited the islands. List the purpose and approximate dates of the visits. Then create a chart to organize the information in a way that is easy to read.

Social Studies

Karana needs courage and resourcefulness to survive alone on the island. What other characteristics and skills does Karana have? Create a head and heart portrait to illustrate the skills Karana uses and the character traits that help her survive. First, draw and cut out a large silhouette of a woman's head. Then cut out a small heart shape. Glue the heart shape onto the bottom fourth of the silhouette. On the silhouette, list skills Karana learns, such as making a seaweed bed. On the heart shape, list the character traits she exhibits, such as courage. Finally, think about your own life and make a head and heart portrait of yourself.

Writing

Reread the section of chapter 12 in which Karana retells a tribal legend about the gods Tumaiyowit and Mukat. The legend explains that people die because Tumaiyowit did. In ancient times, people made up legends like these to explain natural occurrences, such as death. Choose an animal in the book and think about its unusual appearance or behavior. Write and illustrate a legend explaining the reason for its characteristics. For example, why does the devilfish have eight arms?

Language Arts

You have been chosen to lead a scientific team that will study the Island of the Blue Dolphins. First, you need to choose a group of scientists with different specialties to help you complete a thorough study of the island. What types of scientists will you select to be on the team? Obtain a copy of page 38 from your teacher and begin your adventure!

Dolphin Island

Reread the descriptions in the book of the sites listed below. In the space provided, write the page number where each site can be found. Then reread the description of the Island of the Blue Dolphins in chapter 2 and draw a picture of it on the grid. Create a symbol for each of the listed sites and mark its approximate location on your map. Color the map, add a compass rose, and create a legend to explain the symbols you used.

Ghalas-at _____   Coral Cove _____
Wild dogs' cave _____   Sleeping rock _____
Black Cave _____   Aleuts' campsite _____
Karana's house _____   Headland and cave _____
Freshwater springs _____ Sea elephants' home _____

5 boxes = 1 league

Legend

Painting Word Pictures

Directions: Read the information about similes and metaphors below. On the lines provided, write a simile or metaphor for each of the numbered words shown on the unfinished picture. Then illustrate the sentences you wrote by adding details and color to the picture.

Simile: a comparison of two different things using the words *as* or *like*	**Metaphor:** a comparison of two different things without using *as* or *like*
Captain Orlov struck down my father as a snake strikes its prey.	Ramo is a jumping frog, hopping from one spot to another.

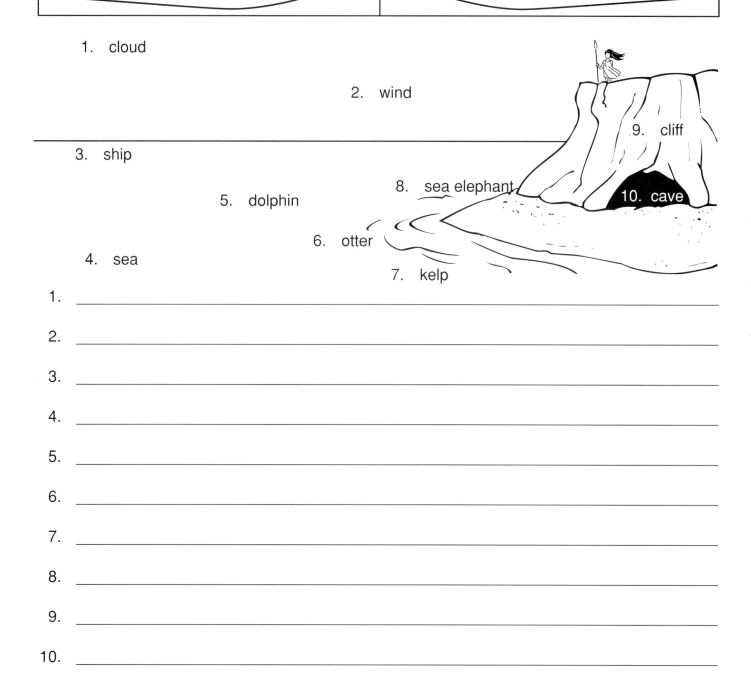

1. cloud

2. wind

3. ship

5. dolphin

4. sea

8. sea elephant

9. cliff

10. cave

6. otter

7. kelp

1. _____

2. _____

3. _____

4. _____

5. _____

6. _____

7. _____

8. _____

9. _____

10. _____

Scientist Expedition

The suffix *-ology* means "the study or science of" and the suffix *-ist* means "one who practices." When the two suffixes are combined into *-ologist*, the suffix means "one who practices the science of." These suffixes are added to Greek and Latin roots to give names to people who study certain branches of science.

Part I Directions: Use a dictionary to identify the field of study for each of the scientists listed on the chart. Write the root and the focus of each scientist's study in the correct columns. An example has been done for you.

Scientist	Root and Meaning	Focus of Study
biologist	*bio:* life	the study of life
1. anthropologist		
2. archaeologist		
3. ichthyologist		
4. entomologist		
5. geologist		
6. herpetologist		
7. toxicologist		
8. marine biologist		
9. oologist		
10. seismologist		

Part II Directions: On separate sheets of paper, write invitations to five scientists asking them to join you on an expedition to study the Island of the Blue Dolphins. In each invitation, state specific reasons why that particular scientist would be interested in joining the team.

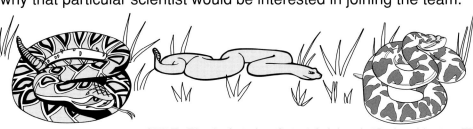

Julie of the Wolves
by Jean Craighead George

About the Book

When an arranged marriage threatens 13-year-old Julie's safety, she packs her belongings and leaves the comforts of home to be with her pen pal in San Francisco. Unfortunately Julie gets lost in the Alaskan wilderness. Drawing upon memories of what her Inuit (Eskimo) father taught her as a child, Julie struggles to survive. Eventually a pack of wolves accepts her as one of its own and helps her stay alive. She realizes that many things she has dreamed about having no longer matter to her. She begins to view her world differently and wonders if she should ever return to civilization.

About the Author

Jean Craighead George was born in 1919 in Washington, DC. Throughout her childhood, her family camped in the woods along the Potomac River. There Jean gained an appreciation for nature. When she was in the third grade, Jean's father, an entomologist, showed her an insect that looked like a twig. The "twig" started walking, inspiring her to write a poem titled "To a Walking Stick." She has been writing ever since.

George went to Penn State University and earned degrees in science and literature. During the 1940s she was a *Washington Post* reporter and part of the White House Press Corps. Over the years, she has kept over 170 animals—such as owls, mink, and tarantulas—in her house and yard! Many of these animals became characters in her books.

While researching a piece on wolves for *Reader's Digest,* George spent time in Alaska observing wolves and actually "talked" to a wolf in its own language. This experience became the springboard for *Julie of the Wolves,* the 1973 Newbery Medal winner.

George has written over 100 books and continues to travel and write. She thoroughly researches her subjects and hopes that children will protect the creatures and places she tells about in her stories.

Student Contract Materials List

- Activity #1: copy of page 42, crayons or colored pencils, map of Alaska
- Activity #2: brown paper grocery bag, crayons or markers, reference materials on Arctic animals
- Activity #3: 5 orange or yellow sentence strips, 1/2 sheet of yellow poster board, scissors, ruler, glue
- Activity #4: copy of page 43, reference materials on weather in Alaska and your town
- Activity #5: paper, pencil
- Activity #6: paper, pencil
- Activity #7: 9" x 12" sheet of light-colored construction paper, crayons or markers

- Activity #8: fine-point marker, pen, graph paper, reference materials on birds, ruler, access to photocopier
- Activity #9: 12" x 18" sheet of light-colored construction paper, reference materials on the Inuit, black marker
- Activity #10: paper, pencil
- Activity #11: drawing paper
- Activity #12: 12" x 18" sheet of blue, red, green, or yellow construction paper; scissors; black marker

Julie of the Wolves

Independent Contract

Name:_____ Number of activities to be completed: _____

Social Studies
1.

The Brooks Range, the Chukchi Sea, and the Arctic Ocean are places discussed in part I that emphasize the barren remoteness of the area in Alaska in which Julie is lost. Obtain a copy of page 42 from your teacher and learn more about the state of Alaska and the untamed region described in *Julie of the Wolves.*

Science
2.

Julie of the Wolves mentions many Arctic animals. Research one of the animals from the list below to discover the following facts: its size, its habitat, its relatives, its food or prey, and its predators. Then tear open a brown grocery bag to make it look like a large animal skin. In the center, write the name of the Arctic animal you researched. Draw illustrations of the animal around its name. Then add your five facts.

caribou	Arctic fox	grizzly bear	wolverine
ground squirrel	moose	lemming	ptarmigan
musk ox	polar bear	walrus	weasel
seal			

Language Arts
3.

Alaska is sometimes known as the Land of the Midnight Sun. To make your own sun, cut out two nine-inch circles from poster board. Then cut five sentence strips in half. Glue the strips to one of the circles to form ten sun rays. Glue the second circle on top of the first, sandwiching the rays between them. Write "Miyax" across the top of the sun and your name across the bottom. On five rays, write phrases that Miyax uses to describe herself in part I. On the other rays, write phrases that describe you.

Science
4.

The caribou migration and the Arctic fox's patches of white fur remind Miyax that winter is on its way. Winter means snow and sub-zero temperatures. Obtain a copy of page 43 from your teacher and, using research materials, compare the climate of Barrow, Alaska, to the climate of your town.

Music
5.

As Miyax observes the wolves paying tribute to Amaroq, she describes him as being wealthy. "The old Eskimo hunters…thought the riches of life were intelligence, fearlessness, and love. A man with these gifts was rich and was a great spirit who was admired in the same way that the gussaks admired a man with money and goods." Do you think the Inuit (Eskimo) or the gussaks (white people) know the true meaning of wealth? Since Miyax expressed many of her feelings in songs, write a short song describing what you think makes someone wealthy.

Critical Thinking
6.

"When fear seizes…change what you are doing. You are doing something wrong." These words of Julie's father return to her as she decides to leave Barrow and gathers enough supplies for a week or so. Think about the things she packs to take with her. If you were packing for a week in the Alaskan tundra, what ten things would you pack? Remember that they have to fit in a backpack. Next to each item, describe why you chose it.

Julie of the Wolves
Independent Contract

Name:_____ Number of activities to be completed: _____

Critical Thinking
7.

Julie sees a hierarchy among the wolves. Amaroq is the leader and Jello is the "low man on the totem pole, the bottom of the ladder." On a sheet of construction paper, sketch either a totem pole or a ladder. Add the names of the wolves to your drawing, placing Amaroq at the top and Jello at the bottom. In between write the names of the other seven wolves, ranking them according to their level of importance in the pack using information from part I of the book. On the back, write a phrase describing each wolf.

Science
8.

Miyax uses birds for many reasons. Research the birds below in order to make a crossword puzzle. Using light pencil marks, plan your crossword on graph paper. Next, write the corresponding clues below the crossword in ink. Use a ruler and a fine-point marker to outline the puzzle. Photocopy the finished puzzle to make an answer key. Then erase the penciled words and make another photocopy. Try out your crossword puzzle to make sure it works.

longspur	bunting	puffin	jaeger
Artctic tern	turnstone	siskin	loon
eider duck	ptarmigan	skua	plover

Social Studies
9.

Miyax and her father, Kapugen, are Inuit (Eskimo). Research the Inuit people and organize the information under the following headings: "Inuit Means…," "Language," "Food," "Hunting," "Land Transportation," "Water Transportation," "Clothing," "Homes," "Important Possessions," "Religion," and "Jobs." Divide a 12" x 18" sheet of construction paper into 12 equal squares and title the first square "INUIT." In each of the remaining squares, write one of the listed headings and the information you found.

Writing
10.

After escaping her arranged marriage, Miyax's goal is to join her pen pal Amy in San Francisco, California. However, after surviving in the tundra she changes her mind. Pretend you are Miyax and write a letter to Amy letting her know why you have changed your mind about your trip to San Francisco.

Language Arts
11.

Kapugen is Miyax's father, but Amaroq becomes her adopted father while she's lost in the Alaskan wilderness. On a sheet of drawing paper, sketch two snowshoes with the oval parts of the shoes overlapping in the center to form a Venn diagram. Title one showshoe "Kapugen" and the other snowshoe "Amaroq." In the center section, compare Kapugen and Amaroq by listing their similarities. In the outer sections, contrast Kapugen and Amaroq by listing their differences.

Writing
12.

The last sentence of the book reads, "Julie pointed her boots toward Kapugen." Choose a sheet of construction paper in a color that matches how you think Julie feels. Use blue if she's sad, red if she's angry, green if she's jealous of Kapugen's gussak wife, and yellow if she's cautious but willing to start a new life. Draw a large boot on the construction paper and cut it out. On the boot, write what you predict Julie will do next. Will she return to Kapugen or is she pointing her boots as a way of placing blame because the "hour of the wolf and the Eskimo is over"?

Far North Features

Obtain a map of Alaska. Then follow the directions below to become familiar with a few features of the far north.

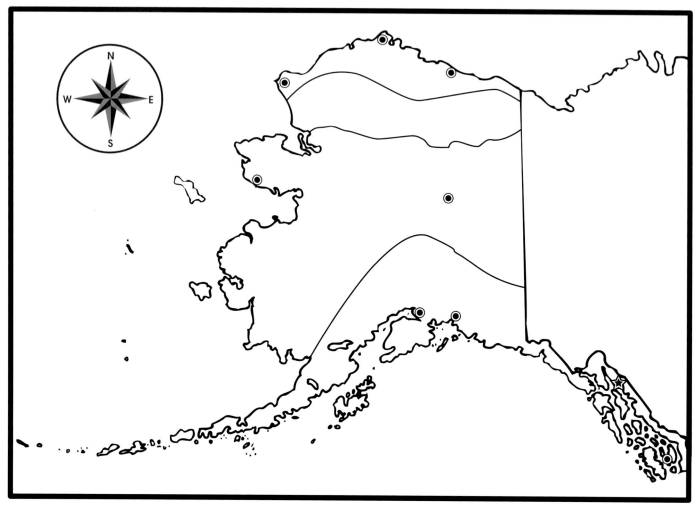

Regions—Label and lightly color the following regions:

Pacific Mountain System (green)
Central Uplands and Lowlands (yellow)
Rocky Mountain System (red)
Arctic Coastal Plain (blue)

Borders—Label the following areas that border Alaska:

Arctic Ocean	Pacific Ocean	Beaufort Sea	Gulf of Alaska
Bering Sea	Bering Strait	Chukchi Sea	Canada

Cities and Towns—Label the following cities and towns:

Point Hope	Anchorage	Fairbanks	Prudhoe Bay	Ketchikan
Barrow	Nome	Juneau	Valdez	

Weather Whiz

Welcome to Weathering Heights University, a school for future climatologists. When completed, the courses below will qualify you as a weather whiz and enable you to compare your climate to Miyax's climate in Barrow, Alaska.

Weather 101

Climate is the average weather of a place over a period of time. Some of the elements that are part of an area's climate include temperature, precipitation, and snow cover. **Assignment:** Use reference materials to help you complete the temperature and precipitation portions of the chart.

Weather 202

Two of the things that influence the climate of an area are its latitude (distance north or south of the equator) and altitude (height above sea level). **Assignment:** Use a globe, world atlas, or other reference materials to help you complete the latitude and altitude sections of the chart.

Weather 303

Climatologists organize similar types of climates into groups. In 1918 Wladimir Koppen introduced a climate classification system, which has been modified into 12 climate groups: tropical wet, tropical wet and dry, semiarid, desert, subtropical dry summer, humid subtropical, humid oceanic, humid continental, subarctic, tundra, icecap, and highland. **Assignment:** Use reference materials to help you fill in the climate group section on the chart.

Congratulations! You are now a graduate of Weathering Heights University and a certified weather whiz!

Climate Comparison Chart

	Barrow, Alaska	Your City, State	Difference
Temperature			
Average January high			
Average January low			
Average July high			
Average July low			
Precipitation			
Days of rain or snow in January			
Days of rain or snow in July			
Latitude			
Altitude			
Climate Group			

©2001 The Education Center, Inc. • *Contracts for Independent Readers • Adventure* • TEC794 • Key p. 63

Note to the teacher: Use with activity #4 on page 40.

My Side of the Mountain
by Jean Craighead George

About the Book

Sam Gribley dislikes living in the crowded New York apartment that he shares with ten other family members. Armed with only a penknife, a ball of cord, an ax, $40, and some flint and steel, Sam runs away to live on his great-grandfather's land in the Catskill Mountains. He quickly learns that surviving alone in the wilderness is not easy, but he rises to the challenges of making fires and finding suitable food. Sam fashions a comfortable home in a large hemlock tree trunk and makes friends with the animals who visit his campsite. He learns to forage for food and prepares ingenious meals for himself each day. Eventually, he captures a baby falcon, Frightful, and trains her to hunt for him. Sam records the details of his survival experience in a journal that takes the reader along on his fascinating adventure.

About the Author

Jean Craighead George was born in 1919 in Washington, DC. During Jean's childhood, her family camped in the woods along the Potomac River. Here Jean gained an appreciation for nature. In the third grade Jean's father, an entomologist, showed her an insect that looked like a twig. The twig started walking, inspiring her to write a poem titled "To a Walking Stick." She has been writing ever since.

George went to Penn State University and earned degrees in science and literature. During the 1940s she was a *Washington Post* reporter and part of the White House Press Corps. Over the years, she has kept over 170 animals—such as owls, mink, and tarantulas—in her house and yard! Many of these animals have become characters in her books. For example, as a teenager she was given a falcon to train; she wrote about the experience in *My Side of the Mountain*. The book, first published in 1959, became a Newbery Honor Book.

George has written over 100 books and continues to travel and write. She thoroughly researches her subjects and hopes that children will desire to protect the creatures and places she tells about in her stories.

Student Contract Materials List

- Activity #1: copy of page 47, white paper, crayons or markers
- Activity #2: 4 sheets of white paper
- Activity #3: white paper, crayons or markers
- Activity #4: 7 index cards, recipe book, stapler, crayons or markers
- Activity #5: copy of page 48, dictionary
- Activity #6: reference materials on poisonous plants, one 12" x 18" sheet of construction paper, black marker
- Activity #7: reference materials on igloo construction, marshmallows or sugar cubes, heavy cardboard, small plastic cup, craft glue
- Activity #8: poetry books containing ballads
- Activity #9: Crayola® Model Magic® modeling compound, painting supplies or markers
- Activity #10: paper, pencil
- Activity #11: copy of page 49, reference materials on vitamins
- Activity #12: reference materials on survival skills; 2 sheets of white paper; colored pencils, crayons, or markers; stapler

My Side of the Mountain

Independent Contract

Name:_____ Number of activities to be completed: _____

1. Math

When Sam tells his father of his plan to run away to live on Great-grandfather Gribley's land, his father relates his own story of running away from home. Sam's father had boarded a ship headed for Singapore, but went back home before the ship sailed. Sam's father loved the sea and eventually did become a sailor. Given a choice, do you think more of your classmates would rather go to sea like Sam's father or live off the land like Sam? Obtain a copy of page 47 from your teacher and learn the answer to this question and more.

2. Art

The simple drawings of plants, tools, and animals found throughout the book help the reader understand Sam's experiences. Look back at several of the drawings, such as the sketch of the deer trap and the smoking rack in the chapter titled "Frightful Learns Her ABC's." Think about how the sketches help you understand the items being described. Then create four sketches that were not illustrated in the book, such as the chimney Sam created for the tree or the process of tanning the deer hide. Write a caption for each picture and share your illustrations with the class.

3. Social Studies

With the help of old maps and books, the local librarian draws maps to help Sam find the Gribley land. What would a map from your school to your home look like? Draw your own map showing the shortest, most direct route between school and home. Add details such as buildings and bodies of water. On a separate sheet of paper, write step-by-step directions describing the route. Check the accuracy of your map by reading your directions as a friend uses your map. If you find that you have left out any steps, revise your directions.

4. Research

In the beginning, Sam has trouble finding enough food to feed his hungry body. Before long, however, he is feasting on acorn pancakes and other woodland delicacies. Make a recipe booklet for three of Sam's favorite foods and three of your own. First, reread sections of the book that contain recipes and serving suggestions for foods such as mussels, venison, and frog soup. Next, copy the directions for preparing the foods on index cards. Then copy three recipes for your own favorite foods. Create a cover with a title, your name, and illustrations. Stack the cards and staple them together along the left edge to complete your booklet.

5. Language Arts

Sam teaches the reader about starting fires with flint and making falcon jesses. Did you understand the words *flint* and *jesses* as you read the book? One way to learn unfamiliar words is to think about their relationships to other words using *analogies,* or sets of words that show relationships by using comparisons. For example, leash is to dog as jess is to falcon. This analogy makes us think that a leash must be similar to a jess and is used to restrain a falcon. Obtain a copy of page 48 from your teacher and learn more about word meanings using analogies.

6. Science

Sam is knowledgeable about edible and poisonous plants. Create a two-column chart showing edible and poisonous plants. To begin, draw a large T on a sheet of construction paper. Label the left-hand column "Edible Plants" and the right-hand column "Poisonous Plants." Use your book to find at least ten plants that Sam eats. List these on the left side of the chart. Then use reference materials to identify at least ten poisonous plants. List these plants and information on their poisonous parts (leaves, berries, roots, etc.) on the right side of the chart.

My Side of the Mountain

Independent Contract

Name: _____ Number of activities to be completed: _____

7. Research

One day Sam decides to build an igloo. He cuts big blocks of snow and sets them in a circle. He isn't able to finish his igloo due to a sudden ice storm. Research igloo construction. Then follow the directions to build your own igloo model. Place a plastic cup in the center of a sheet of heavy cardboard to support your structure. Use marshmallows or sugar cubes and glue to construct the igloo. Finally, write out the steps you followed and share your research and model with the class.

8. Writing

After Sam bathes in the icy spring water, he sings songs that he makes up. Imagine bathing in water that is so cold it takes your breath away. Read several examples of ballads in poetry books before you begin to write. Then write a *ballad,* or a narrative poem that may be sung, containing at least two four-line stanzas describing the chilling experience. The ballad's lines should contain good rhythm, but do not have to rhyme. Include a *refrain,* or a phrase, line, or verse that is repeated at intervals, in your ballad. Perform your ballad for the class as a poem or set to the music of a familiar song.

9. Art

Bando makes jars from clay that he finds near the stream. Using Crayola® Model Magic® modeling compound, construct a pot and a lid. First, flatten and shape a lump of clay to form the bottom of the pot. Then roll lumps of clay into snakelike lengths. Form rings and stack them to create the pot. Create a lid that is slightly larger than the pot's diameter in the same way you formed the bottom. Smooth the clay sides of the pot. After your masterpiece has dried, decorate it with markers or paint.

10. Writing

It's almost Halloween and Sam has been competing with the local animals to collect nuts, apples, and other precious foods to store away for the winter. Sam decides to treat his companions to a Halloween party and issues an invitation to them by leaving food outside. Soon the message gets around and animals flock to the party. As the moon rises the following night, the party gets out of control. Reread the account of the wild party in "We All Learn About Halloween." Then choose an animal— such as the red fox, skunk, or raccoon—and rewrite the story of the party from your chosen animal's point of view.

11. Science

Sam keeps track of his health and, with winter upon him, he notices that he hasn't even had a cold! In January, though, Sam begins to notice fatigue and sore joints. Suddenly he finds himself craving liver and realizes that rabbit liver seems to help him feel better. Later, Sam learns that liver is high in vitamin C, a vitamin found in the green vegetables and fruits that Sam doesn't have. Obtain a copy of page 49 from your teacher and learn more about the vitamins that humans need.

12. Research

Sam prepares for his adventure by reading about wilderness survival. Research to learn tips or guidelines for three survival skills, such as starting a fire without matches, building a shelter, and finding food. Create a step book by stacking two sheets of paper so that the bottom edges of the sheets are one inch apart. Then fold the stack in half so that the top edges are one inch from the bottom edges, creating steps. Staple the book along the folded edge. On the top sheet, create a decorative cover. On each of the next three pages, list step-by-step directions and illustrations for each survival skill.

Name _____

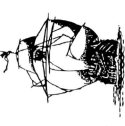

By Land or by Sea

Sam's Great-grandfather Gribley became a sailor after his farm failed. Sam's father used to say, "The land is no place for a Gribley." Looking back over his adventure, Sam thinks that the land is "just the place for a Gribley." Do you think more people would prefer life on the land or the sea?

Directions: Use the questions on the chart below to interview 15 classmates. Record each response with a check mark. Then total the check marks. On a separate sheet of paper, create a colorful bar graph showing the results of your survey.

Would you rather...

		1	2	3	4	5	6	7	8	9	10	11	12	13	14	15	Total
1.	a.	keep a journal on tree bark?															
	b.	keep a journal in a notebook?															
2.	a.	train a falcon to hunt?															
	b.	train a parrot to talk?															
3.	a.	eat acorn pancakes with blueberry jam?															
	b.	eat foods from many lands?															
4.	a.	live in a tree trunk alone?															
	b.	live on a ship with others?															
5.	a.	get vitamin C from rabbit liver?															
	b.	get vitamin C from citrus fruits?															
6.	a.	live alone on a mountain?															
	b.	travel around the world?															
7.	a.	trap deer, rabbits, and other animals?															
	b.	catch tuna, cod, and other fish?															
8.	a.	wear deer and rabbit skin clothes?															
	b.	wear rain gear and boots?															
9.	a.	wait out a snowstorm inside a hollow tree?															
	b.	wait out a hurricane below a ship's deck?															
10.	a.	cook over an open fire?															
	b.	cook in the galley of a ship?															

©2001 The Education Center, Inc. • *Contracts for Independent Readers • Adventure •* TEC794

Note to the teacher: Use with activity #1 on page 45.

47

Name_____

Analogy Adventure

An *analogy* shows a relationship between two objects that are otherwise unlike. Focus closely on each analogy below. Think about the relationship between the words in the first pair. Use a dictionary to look up any words that are unfamiliar. Then choose a word from the word bank to complete the analogy. **Hint:** Notice the symbols that represent the words *is to* and *as* in the example below.

Example:	Marble **is to** basketball **as** pebble **is to** _____.
	marble : basketball :: pebble : _____
Think:	Marbles and basketballs are both balls, but a basketball is much larger. What is much larger than a pebble but is still a rock?
Answer:	boulder

Word Bank

warden	venison	steep	avalanche	mountains	plunge	talons	gorge
cache	ponder	chew	bough	lure	chute	tuber	

1. bush : shrub :: bait : _ _ _ _

2. money : bank :: nuts : _ _ _ _ _ _

3. deer : _ _ _ _ _ _ _ _ :: cow : beef

4. rain : flood :: snow : _ _ _ _ _ _ _ _ _

5. potato : _ _ _ _ _ _ :: tomato : fruit

6. gnaw : _ _ _ _ :: maneuver : steer

7. Hawaii : islands :: Catskills : _ _ _ _ _ _ _ _ _

8. shoot : _ _ _ _ _ _ :: threw : through

9. bear : claws :: falcon : _ _ _ _ _ _

10. think : _ _ _ _ _ _ _ :: gather : harvest

11. dive : _ _ _ _ _ _ _ :: fly : soar

12. city : police officer :: park : _ _ _ _ _ _

13. sea : fjord :: land : _ _ _ _ _ _

14. _ _ _ _ _ _ : tree :: tributary : river

15. soak : _ _ _ _ _ _ :: linger : stay

©2001 The Education Center, Inc. • *Contracts for Independent Readers* • *Adventure* • TEC794 • Key p. 64

48 Note to the teacher: Use with activity #5 on page 45.

Naturally Nutritious Foods

Part I Directions: The human body needs 13 vitamins, some of which the body produces itself. Research the vitamins listed below. Then describe how each vitamin is beneficial to the body. Finally, list the food sources for each vitamin. The first one has been done for you.

Vitamin	Benefit to the Human Body	Food Sources
Vitamin D	The human body needs it to *metabolize,* or make use of, food that is eaten.	eggs, fortified milk, tuna, and salmon
Vitamin E		
Vitamin A		
Vitamin B$_1$		
Vitamin B$_2$		
Vitamin B$_6$		
Vitamin B$_{12}$		
Folic acid		
Vitamin C		

Part II Directions: List ten foods that you have eaten this week and the vitamins found in each food. Check to see if you listed every vitamin from the chart. If not, list foods that you could include in your diet next week in order to get all the vitamins your body needs.

Note to the teacher: Use with activity #11 on page 46.

Stone Fox

by John Reynolds Gardiner

About the Book

Little Willy and his grandfather live together on a potato farm in Wyoming. Willy's grandfather becomes sick at heart and won't get out of bed when the government threatens to take away the farm to pay $500 in back taxes. Ten-year-old Willy is determined to save the farm by entering the National Dogsled Race with Searchlight, his lifelong companion. If they can win the race, they will be awarded the $500 that Willy so desperately needs. Willy and Searchlight must race against experienced dogsled teams, including the legendary Indian Stone Fox and his beautiful Samoyeds. Stone Fox is favored to win, but Willy confidently practices with Searchlight every day. In the poignant, beautifully written ending, Willy wins the race at a terrible cost.

About the Author

As a child, John Reynolds Gardiner was something of a rebel. Since his mother wanted him to read, he refused to read. In fact, he was 19 before he read his first novel. Not to be dissuaded, John's mother read to him every night. He pretended not to listen, but was secretly enthralled. John was not a good speller and his writing was poor. Therefore, he was not successful in English classes in school. John did have an imagination and, eventually, he wrote a story about a boy and his dog that was published. That book was *Stone Fox*.

Gardiner earned a master's degree in engineering from the University of California, Los Angeles, and works as an aerospace engineer for McDonnell Douglas Corporation. He still writes—on his lunch break! Gardiner is married and has three daughters.

Stone Fox has sold over 150,000 copies and has won several awards. In 1987, it was made into an NBC television movie. Other works by Gardiner include *Top Secret, General Butterfingers, Mr. Popper's Penguins,* and *Alto Secreto*.

Note: No photo of John Reynolds Gardiner is available.

Student Contract Materials List

- Activity #1: copy of page 53; reference materials on the cotton gin, threshing machine, sulky plow, and reaping machine
- Activity #2: sprouted potato, clean 2-liter plastic bottle, shallow dish, scissors, potting soil, water, journal
- Activity #3: crayons or markers
- Activity #4: copy of page 54, 9" x 12" sheet of construction paper, colored pencils, scissors, glue
- Activity #5: ½ sheet of poster board, research materials on Samoyed dogs, crayons or markers
- Activity #6: seven 4½" x 6" sheets of black construction paper, white-colored pencil, stapler
- Activity #7: copy of page 55
- Activity #8: 12" x 18" sheet of light-colored construction paper, colored pencils
- Activity #9: reference materials on the Shoshone tribe
- Activity #10: reference materials on potato production, 9" x 12" sheet of construction paper, glue, scissors, crayons or markers
- Activity #11: ½ sheet of poster board, 3" x 5" index cards, scissors, crayons or markers
- Activity #12: 12" x 18" sheet of white construction paper

Stone Fox

Independent Contract

Name:_____ Number of activities to be completed: _____

 1. **Social Studies**

Without money to rent a plow horse, little Willy has to find another way to harvest the potato crop. Reread chapter 2 in which little Willy and Searchlight work for more than ten days to finish the job. Little Willy doesn't have the benefit of modern farming machinery to help him. Farm work has been made easier by inventions such as the cotton gin, threshing machine, sulky plow, and the reaping machine. Obtain a copy of page 53 from your teacher and learn more about these inventions that have improved farming methods.

 2. **Science**

Learn more about potato plants by growing one yourself! Obtain a piece of potato that has sprouted. Have an adult use scissors to cut the top third off a two-liter plastic bottle and then punch several drainage holes in the bottom. Place the bottle in a shallow dish. Plant the sprouted potato piece in one cup of soil in the bottle and set it in a sunny window. Add water and soil as the plant grows, keeping the dirt level just beneath the plant's lowest leaves. Observe the plant for several weeks, describing its changes in a journal. Then pull the plant out of the soil and look for baby potatoes near the roots.

 3. **Math**

Potatoes are nutritious and delicious! What are some favorite ways to eat them? Survey at least 20 classmates to find out their potato favorites, such as french fries, baked potatoes, mashed potatoes, hash browns, and others. Use the data you collect to create a bar or line graph to show the results of the survey.

 4. **Writing**

As you read *Stone Fox,* were you able to feel Willy's love for his grandfather and his concern about saving the farm? Think about Willy's problems and emotions. Then think about a time when you were concerned about someone or something. The feelings, reactions, and other characteristics of real and fictional people can be expressed in biopoems. Obtain a copy of page 54 from your teacher and follow the directions to complete a biopoem for yourself and one for a character from *Stone Fox.*

 5. **Research**

Stone Fox has a team of Samoyed dogs to pull his sled. Samoyeds are muscular and intelligent with beautiful long white hair. Research this special breed to learn more about their characteristics, intellect, and uses. Use this information to design and illustrate a poster advertising the sale of a team of Samoyeds like Stone Fox's. Include a detailed description of the dogs, including reasons that someone might want to purchase them.

 6. **Language Arts**

Grandfather uses familiar sayings, such as "Where there's a will, there's a way," to teach little Willy important lessons for life. Make your own collection of "Lessons for Life." Find three of Grandfather's sayings in the book. Write each one on a separate sheet of black paper, using a white-colored pencil to resemble writing on a chalkboard. Then interview several older people, asking them to share sayings that they know. Write three of these sayings on separate sheets of black paper. Create a cover with a title and your name. Stack the pages and staple the booklet along one edge.

Stone Fox

Independent Contract

Name:_____ Number of activities to be completed: _____

---

 7. | **Math**

Dogsled teams like Stone Fox's require a lot of equipment for comfort and safety. Pretend you need to outfit a team of six Alaskan malamutes. First, you will need to purchase the necessary equipment. Obtain a copy of page 55 from your teacher and follow the directions to complete the activity.

 8. **Social Studies**

When Willy enters the race, Mayor Smiley gives him a map showing the ten-mile route. Reread chapter 9 and use the details to create your own map of the route for the race. Include important landmarks such as the lake and Grandfather's house. Remember to create a map key and a compass rose. Add pictures of Willy and other important characters from the book. Then color your map.

---

 9. **Language Arts**

Stone Fox is a member of the Shoshone tribe. His people, a peaceful tribe of seed gatherers, had been forced to leave their homeland in Utah and settle on a reservation in Wyoming with the Arapaho tribe. Stone Fox's dream is to return his people to their original lands. Research the Shoshone tribe to learn about its way of life and homeland before the arrival of the Europeans in America. Pretend you are Stone Fox. Write a persuasive letter to the president of the United States describing your tribe's history and asking that your people be allowed to return to their homeland in Utah.

 10. **Social Studies**

Potatoes originally came from South America. Today, the potato is grown in most countries around the world and is one of the most important foods. Research to learn about worldwide potato production. List the major potato-growing countries of the world and the amount of potatoes each country produces in a year. Create a bar graph to illustrate the data. Then list the major potato-growing states in the United States and each state's potato production. Create a second bar graph to show this data. Cut out your graphs and glue them to a sheet of construction paper, labeling each one.

---

 11. **Critical Thinking**

Create a board game using the National Dogsled Race as the theme. Design a gameboard trail that is similar to the race route in the book. Plan and create character game pieces and game cards that provide ways for players to move forward and backward. For example, "Sell 100 pounds of potatoes. Move forward three spaces," or "Fallen tree across track. Go backward two spaces." Write a set of directions including how many players are needed, how to decide which player goes first, and how the game is won. When you are finished, invite classmates to play the game with you.

 12. **Writing**

Little Willy enters the National Dogsled Race that takes place in Jackson, Wyoming, in February. Before the race, he reads newspaper stories about his competitors. Stone Fox is the most famous participant and is favored to win, but the others have good racing records and excellent dog teams as well. Reread the account of the race in chapter 9. Design a newspaper front page for that day. Write and illustrate at least three news articles, including at least one article about the outcome of the race. Be creative, but make sure your stories accurately represent the time and setting of the novel.

Inventions in Agriculture

Patents are issued by the United States government to protect the rights of inventors. The owner of a patent is the only person who can produce and sell the patented item.

Directions: Use reference materials to research the inventions shown on the patent applications below. Fill out the modified patent application for each inventor. Then draw a sketch of each invention and attach the sketches to this sheet.

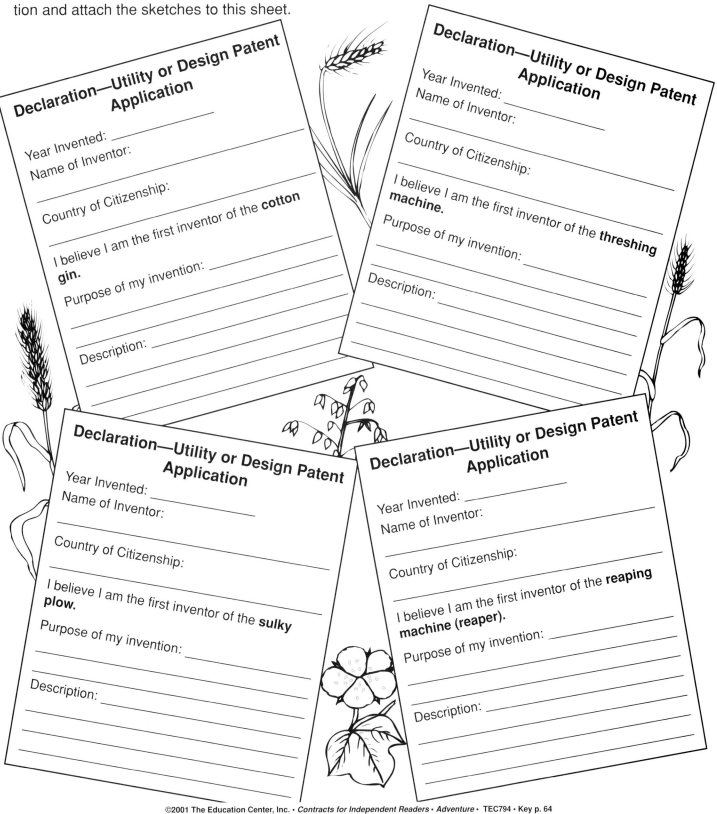

Declaration—Utility or Design Patent Application

Year Invented: _____
Name of Inventor: _____

Country of Citizenship: _____

I believe I am the first inventor of the **cotton gin.**

Purpose of my invention: _____

Description: _____

Declaration—Utility or Design Patent Application

Year Invented: _____
Name of Inventor: _____

Country of Citizenship: _____

I believe I am the first inventor of the **threshing machine.**

Purpose of my invention: _____

Description: _____

Declaration—Utility or Design Patent Application

Year Invented: _____
Name of Inventor: _____

Country of Citizenship: _____

I believe I am the first inventor of the **sulky plow.**

Purpose of my invention: _____

Description: _____

Declaration—Utility or Design Patent Application

Year Invented: _____
Name of Inventor: _____

Country of Citizenship: _____

I believe I am the first inventor of the **reaping machine (reaper).**

Purpose of my invention: _____

Description: _____

Note to the teacher: Use with activity #1 on page 51.

People in Poetry

A biopoem uses a specific format to give basic information about a person's character traits and personality.

Directions: On a separate sheet of paper, write two biopoems using the format given below. Describe yourself in one poem and a character from *Stone Fox* in the second poem. Proofread and edit your work. Then copy the poems onto the silhouettes below. When you are finished, cut out the silhouettes and glue them to a sheet of construction paper.

Biopoem Format

Line 1:   First name
Line 2:   Four adjectives describing the person
Line 3:   Relative of (brother, sister, daughter, son, cousin, etc.)
Line 4:   Lover of (list three things or people)
Line 5:   Who feels (list three emotions)

Line 6:   Who needs (list three things)
Line 7:   Who fears (list three things)
Line 8:   Who gives (list three things)
Line 9:   Who would like to see (list three things or places)
Line 10: Resident of
Line 11: Last name or nickname

_____

_____

Relative of _____

Lover of _____

Who feels _____

Who needs _____

Who fears _____

Who gives _____

Who would like to see _____

Resident of _____

_____

_____

_____

Relative of _____

Lover of _____

Who feels _____

Who needs _____

Who fears _____

Who gives _____

Who would like to see _____

Resident of _____

_____

©2001 The Education Center, Inc. • *Contracts for Independent Readers* • *Adventure* • TEC794

54   **Note to the teacher:** Use with activity #4 on page 51.

Name_____ *Stone Fox*

A Costly Team

Outfitting a dogsled team can be very expensive. Imagine that you need to outfit a team of six Alaskan malamutes. Then follow the directions below to calculate the cost.

Directions: Study the lists of required equipment shown below. Calculate the subtotal value of each list. Then calculate the total value of the investment that you would need to make. **Hint:** You will need to purchase more than one unit of some items, such as the collars and booties.

Sled and Sled Dog Equipment

1 sled	$769.00
6 harnesses	$18.00 each
2 flashing light collars	$14.50 each
4 collars	$3.75 each
48 booties	$1.20 each
1 day bag	$75.00
2 cable ganglines	
one 4-dog section	$45.00
one 2-dog section	$30.00
1 picket line (6-dog)	$75.00
3 stake-out cables	$7.00 each

Subtotal: _____

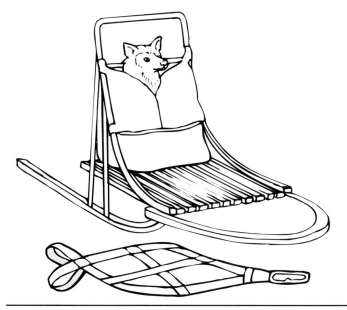

Survival Supplies

1 ax	$18.00
1 ax cover	$3.50
2 boxes of matches	
(or 2 lighters)	$1.50 each
1 cookstove and fuel	$99.95
1 compass	$9.75
12 pounds of dog food	$1.85 per pound

Subtotal: _____

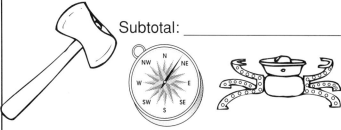

Musher Equipment

1 pair of snowshoes	
with bindings	$99.00
1 cold-weather	
sleeping bag	$519.00
1 headlamp	$46.00
3 pairs of gloves	$5.00 per pair

Subtotal: _____

Your sponsor will also give you $350.00 for miscellaneous supplies, such as warm clothing, food, and water.

Total Investment: _____

Note to the teacher: Use with activity #7 on page 52.

Williwaw!
by Tom Bodett

About the Book

At 12 and 13, Ivan and September Crane are able to take care of themselves while their dad, a fisherman, is away for a week. Their father radios home saying that he will be fishing for another two weeks and that they are to stay off the bay and not hook up video games to the radio battery. If they can't do these things, they will have to stay with their Aunt Nelda. They agree to their dad's conditions, but Ivan breaks his word and ends up frying both of the radios. Because it is too dangerous to stay in their cove without a working radio, Ivan and September break the rest of the agreement and go across the bay to get the radios repaired. After several trips across the bay, they are caught in the middle of the bay in a violent storm—a williwaw!

About the Author

Tom Bodett moved to Alaska from Michigan in 1976. He has lived in Alaska for more than 20 years. Bodett began working in the construction trade as an independent house builder.

When he wrote a commentary on cold-turkey tobacco withdrawal, his work drew attention and led to similar jobs, including several radio appearances. Within three months, Bodett had a spot as a regular commentator on National Public Radio's news program *All Things Considered*.

Bodett's first book, *As Far As You Can Go Without a Passport: The View From the End of the Road* (a collection of radio commentaries), was published in 1985. Now Bodett has six books and 15 audio recordings to his credit. Bodett is perhaps best known as the spokesman for Motel 6, a role he has had for 13 years. During his first recording with Motel 6, Bodett ad-libbed the now famous tag line "We'll leave the light on for you." *Williwaw!* is Bodett's first book for young readers.

Student Contract Materials List

- Activity #1: paper, pencil
- Activity #2: paper, pencil
- Activity #3: crayons or markers, 12" x 18" sheet of light-colored construction paper
- Activity #4: 12" x 18" sheet of construction paper, crayons or markers, glue, old magazines, scissors
- Activity #5: 1½" x 9" strips of green, blue, red, and purple construction paper; research materials on orcas, bears, and eagles; stapler
- Activity #6: copy of page 59, dictionary
- Activity #7: crayons or markers, four 4" x 6" index cards, hole puncher, ribbon
- Activity #8: crayons or markers, nine 3" x 5" index cards, hole puncher, tape, 5' length of yarn
- Activity #9: 9" x 12" sheet of light-colored construction paper; research materials on the Trans-Alaska Pipeline, the Alaska fishing industry, and the Inuit; scissors
- Activity #10: tape recorder, blank cassette tape
- Activity #11: crayons or markers, white paper
- Activity #12: copy of page 60, map of Alaska

Williwaw!

Independent Contract

Name: _____   Number of activities to be completed: _____

---

1. ## Writing

Ivan and September argue about a weather rhyme: "Red sky at night, the sailors delight. Red sky in the morning, the sailors take warning." This old saying helps people predict the weather. Write your own poem or rhyme to help yourself remember something or predict something. List the steps it requires in order; then rewrite them as a rhyme. For example, if you have a hard time remembering to press 1 when calling long distance, you could write a rhyme that says, "Long distance is fun, but first press 1."

2. ## Math

Ivan and September spend several days digging clams in order to make enough money to fix their radios. Ivan estimates that it takes 20 clams to make a pound and that each pound sells for one dollar. Each bucket holds ten pounds of clams. Ivan and September need to make $60. Pretend they find four clams every minute. Using this information, make up four story problems. Write the problems on one side of your paper and the solutions on the other side.

3. ## Social Studies

Ivan and September need a thorough knowledge of Bag Bay to be able to navigate it using only a compass. Reread the description of Bag Bay in chapter 9. Then make a map that includes Bag Bay, Steamer Cove, Cape Protection, Point Thumb, and the Gulf of Alaska. Include at least three more places from the story and a compass rose. Add other details about events that happen in the different places.

4. ## Art

Bush rats and townies don't have much in common. TC helps bring them together through his interest in September's and Ivan's lives. Make a collage comparing townies and bush rats. Label one half of a piece of construction paper "Bush Rats" and the other half "Townies." Then glue pictures that show the rustic, natural life of the Crane family on the bush rats side. On the other side, glue pictures representing the life and interests of the town kids. Title your collage "The Kids of Bag Bay."

5. ## Science

Orcas, bears, and eagles appear in *Williwaw!* Research these animals' food chains. Then use 1½" x 9" strips of green, blue, red, and purple construction paper to represent links in each animal's food chain: green for *producers,* blue for *herbivores,* red for *carnivores,* and purple for *omnivores.* Use the information from your research to label each strip with the appropriate plant or animal in each food chain, with the orca, bear, or eagle at the top of that chain. Use at least three links in each food chain and staple them together. For example, eagle (red) eats chipmunk (purple) eats grasshopper (blue) eats grass (green).

6. ## Language Arts

Williwaw! takes place on Bag Bay, so boats are an important part of the story. Obtain a copy of page 59 from your teacher and complete the activity using vocabulary from the story.

Williwaw!

Independent Contract

Name: _____ Number of activities to be completed: _____

 7. | **Language Arts**

In chapter 6, Ivan and September compare foods from their side of the bay and from town. They decide that there are good foods on both sides of the bay. Make a list of your three favorite foods. Then write the recipes for those foods on index cards, listing the major ingredients, the directions for making the dishes, and the reasons the foods are your favorites. Title and decorate a cover on a separate index card. When finished, punch a hole in the upper left-hand corner of each card and tie them together with ribbon.

 8. | **Social Studies**

In *Williwaw!,* a lot happens in nine days. Make a timeline of the events. Punch a hole in the top two corners of nine index cards. Then thread a piece of yarn through the holes so that the nine cards are hanging end to end from the yarn. Tape the yarn ends to the first and last cards so the cards stay on the yarn. Label the top of the first index card "Friday," the next "Saturday," and so on until all are labeled. On each card list that day's events and illustrate each event on the back. Write your name on the first card.

 9. | **Writing**

Alaska is home to the Trans-Alaska Pipeline, a huge fishing industry, and the Inuit. Research these three topics. Then write a story using your research. After you have proofread your story, cut out a large shape from construction paper to represent an item from your story, such as an oil rig, a fish, or an igloo. Copy your story onto the cutout shape.

 10. | **Language Arts**

The disappearance and rescue of Ivan and September Crane in the williwaw are major events in the Bag Bay area. Write a script for a headline news report of these events for KBAG radio. Include segments of interviews with Mr. Crane, Harry, Ivan, and September. Then find some friends or family members to play each part and help you read the script while you tape-record it. Replay the radio news broadcast for your class.

 11. | **Critical Thinking**

Harry says that an old seaman told him you should name a boat for the thing you fear the most or the thing you miss the most. Because Harry fears a williwaw more than anything, he names his boat *Williwaw.* If you could have a boat, what would you name it? Draw a picture of the kind of boat you'd like to have. Choose a name for your boat and write it on your drawing. Then write a brief description of your boat and an explanation of why you have chosen its name.

 12. | **Social Studies**

A diverse array of landforms covers Alaska's landscape. Obtain a map of Alaska and a copy of page 60 from your teacher, and learn more about Alaska's terrain.

Ships Ahoy!

Boats are prominent features of *Williwaw!* Sometimes, though, it's hard to picture what the author is referring to when he uses boat terms. Use this activity to help you understand boats, and their vocabulary, a little better.

Directions: Read the passage below. Choose the appropriate word from the list at the bottom of the page to fit into each of the blanks in the passage. Cross off each vocabulary word as it is used. When all of the blanks are filled, write the definitions of the remaining words on the back of this sheet. Use *Williwaw!* or a dictionary to help you if needed.

Harry steers his boat, *Williwaw,* around the boulders at the entrance to Steamer Cove. Ivan and

September stand on their _____ and watch his approach. They can see Harry inside the
                                    1

_____ as he waves to them. As he eases up to the dock, he walks onto the _____
          2   3

of his boat and tosses Ivan a line. Ivan secures the line to the dock _____ and then hops
                                                                                              4

over the cap rail onto Harry's deck to take the handful of mail Harry is holding. A blue and white

flag hangs from the _____ of Harry's boat, and the boat rocks back and forth as its
                              5

_____ side bumps gently against the dock. Before leaving, Harry goes down into his
          6

_____ to retrieve a large manila envelope addressed to Ivan and September Crane.
          7

September is happy to receive the home-schooling packet, but Ivan scowls at it. Harry laughs at

the children, then checks the ropes of his _____ and adjusts his sails before pulling away
                                                            8

from the dock.

The next morning, Ivan and September climb into their small, wooden _____ (or dinghy)
                                                                                              9

and head for the clam bed on the other side of the cove. September steers through the fog with

one hand clamped tightly to the _____ and the other gripping her compass. As they near
                                            10

the bank, September cuts the _____ motor and Ivan steers them in using the _____.
                                          11   12

September tosses the _____ to the shore, and Ivan climbs out and secures the *Four-O-Five*
                              13

to a large boulder. Then they collect their buckets from the boat and begin their quest for clams.

pilothouse	dock	skiff	keel	towline
dinghy	oars	deck	tiller	rigging
cleat	cabin	mast	oarlock	starboard
outboard	hull	galley	scuppers	

Amazing Alaska

Use a map to help you label each of the geographic features listed below in the correct location on the outline map of Alaska. Label the capital city of Alaska and the largest city in Alaska. Then find ten more important land-marks in Alaska and label them.

Alaska Peninsula	Gulf of Alaska
Alaska Range	Kenai Fjords
Alexander Archipelago	Kobuk Valley
Arctic Ocean	Kodiak Island
Baird Mountains	Mount McKinley
Beaufort Sea	Norton Sound
Bering Strait	Port Graham
Bristol Bay	Malaspina Glacier
Cape Newenham	Yukon River
Cook Inlet	

*Aleutian Islands not shown on this map.

Note to the teacher: Use with activity #12 on page 58.

Books That Will Take You on the Adventure of a Lifetime

Thrive in the wilderness, traipse through the jungle, endure a natural disaster, and survive a cave-in with this collection of adventure novels.

Beardance by Will Hobbs • Cloyd feels closer to the grizzly bear than he does to any person he knows. Now it is up to him to save what may be the only two grizzly cubs left in Colorado.

The Fear Place by Phyllis Reynolds Naylor • Although Doug loves to be outdoors camping and hiking, he refuses to revisit the place that he fears the most—a two-foot-wide ledge on the side of a cliff. But when his brother doesn't come back from his hike for several days, will he be able to face his fears and save his brother?

The Incredible Journey by Sheila Burnford • An old bull terrier, a young Labrador retriever, and a haughty Siamese cat are on their way to find their owners. It is cold and they have a long way to go, but they are determined to make it or die trying.

Jaguar by Roland Smith • Jacob has joined his father in Brazil to help him set up a jaguar preserve. Once there, Jacob realizes that there is more at stake than saving the jaguars—like saving his father and himself.

Night of the Twisters by Ivy Ruckman • What seems like just another ordinary day turns into one that will "mess up your life," as Dan Hatch puts it. Will he and his buddies survive the night of the twisters?

Poppy by Avi • Poppy, a tiny deer mouse, must overcome her fear of the evil great horned owl Ocax in order to save her family.

Quake! by Joe Cottonwood • Franny, Jennie, and Sidney are at home alone when an earthquake strikes. Now they must find it in themselves to help each other and help the neighbors—and put their life back in some kind of order.

The Return of Santa Paws by Nicholas Edwards • The plane has crashed and their uncle is hurt too much to move very far. Now it is up to Gregory, Patricia, and their dog Santa Paws to find help.

Stranded by Ben Mikaelsen • Missing one foot, Koby Easton is self-conscious about her appearance. When she discovers two beached pilot whales, she stays up all night trying to save them. Through helping them, she begins to help herself—as the whales get better, so does Koby.

Survival! Cave-In (St. Claire, Pennsylvania, 1859) by K. Duey and K. A. Bale • Rory has come up with a plan to earn some money and help the Quinns. The only problem is that to do this, she must work in the mines that killed her father and brother.

White Water by P. J. Petersen • Greg must save his father, who has been bitten by a rattlesnake. To do that, he will have to accept his half brother James, overcome his fears, and brave the rapids.

Ziggy and the Black Dinosaurs by Sharon M. Draper • Ziggy, Rico, Jerome, and Rashawn have nothing to do for the summer until they decide to start their own club—The Black Dinosaurs. Now they have secret passwords, a mascot, treasures, a clubhouse, and a case to solve.

Answer Keys

Page 8

1. atoll: a ring of coral surrounding a lagoon
2. foothill: a hill at the foot of higher hills; a hilly region at the base of a mountain range
3. island: an area of land surrounded by water
4. islet: a little island
5. beach: a shore covered by sand, gravel, or larger rock fragments
6. lagoon: a shallow sound, channel, or pond connected to a larger body of water
7. mountain: a steep-sided landform that is higher than a hill
8. plateau: a level surface that rises steeply above the surrounding land
9. barrier reef: a coral reef separated from a shore by a lagoon
10. sea: a great body of salty water covering much of the earth
11. valley: a low area of land between hills or mountains
12. volcano: an opening in the earth that forces out lava, rock, gases, and ash

Page 9

Students' responses will vary. Possible responses are listed below.

1. Mafatu makes a knife out of whale bone, a spear from a stone spear point and a wooden shaft, and fish traps out of bamboo.
2. Mafatu finds a freshwater stream. He catches fish and lobsters, gathers fruit, and kills a wild boar.
3. Mafatu makes a lean-to, which he later turns into a three-wall shelter.
4. After Mafatu strips bark from a mulberry tree, he wets the fibers and pounds them into cloth to make a pareu.
5. Mafatu makes a raft out of bamboo poles, a canoe from a tamanu tree, and sails from woven plant fibers.

Page 15

Students' responses will vary. Possible responses are listed below.

1. Person vs. Person (Red): Faced with Timothy's unwillingness to drink too much of the water on the raft, Phillip begins to dislike him.
2. Person vs. Self (Yellow): Phillip discovers he is blind.
3. Person vs. Person (Red): Phillip becomes angry with Timothy for making him weave sleeping mats while blind.
4. Person vs. Nature (Blue): A hurricane passes over the small cay.
5. Person vs. Self (Yellow): Phillip is angry at Timothy for leaving him on the island alone after he has died.
6. Person vs. Nature (Blue): While swimming in the fishing hole, Phillip is attacked by a moray eel.
7. Person vs. Self (Yellow): Phillip knows that he cannot survive on the island blind and alone. The thought makes him miserable.
8. Person vs. Self (Yellow): Phillip listens as a plane passes over the island and then leaves. Phillip wishes he were dead.

Page 16

1. False	9. True
2. True	10. False
3. True	11. True
4. False	12. False
5. True	13. False
6. False	14. True
7. True	15. True
8. False	

HAMMERHEAD SHARK

Page 20

Students' responses will vary. Possible responses are listed below.

Before

1. dependent
2. attends formalized school
3. lives in government housing
4. uses store-bought goods
5. uses snowmobile for transportation

After

1. independent, self-sufficient
2. learns from the "school of life"
3. lives in an animal skin tent
4. uses only handmade goods
5. uses dogsled for transportation

Page 21

Students' responses will vary. Possible responses are listed below.

chapter 2: You don't get a song. You are a song.

chapter 3: Always take care of your dogs first.

chapter 4: In some ways, dogs are smarter than men, if they're just allowed to be dogs.

chapter 5: To become a man, you cannot go home. Leave and run with the dogs so you can become what you want to be.

chapter 8: The best fat to eat is also the best fat to burn in your lamp. Save the best for the fire and you will not be cold.

chapter 10: It isn't the destination that counts. It is the journey, so pay attention to it.

chapter 12: To be close to death and then come back cannot be accomplished without pain.

chapter 14: Dogs run because they want to, or because they think they want to. You can make them think they want to run.

Page 25

Students' vocabulary words and definitions will vary. Accept all reasonable responses.

1. windlass: a machine used for hoisting or hauling
2. berth: a place to sit or sleep on a ship or vehicle
3. taffeta: a crisp, lustrous fabric used for women's clothing
4. tarpaulin: a piece of material used for protecting exposed objects or areas
8. threshold: the place of entering; gate, doorway
10. valiantly: carried out with courage or determination

Answer Keys

Page 26

High Tide

Mon.	Tues.	Wed.	Thurs.
5:00 A.M.	5:50 A.M.	6:40 A.M.	7:30 A.M.
5:25 P.M.	6:15 P.M.	7:05 P.M.	7:55 P.M.

Low Tide

Mon.	Tues.	Wed.	Thurs.
11:13 A.M.	12:03 P.M.	12:53 P.M.	1:43 P.M.
11:38 P.M.	12:28 A.M.	1:18 A.M.	2:08 A.M.

1. 1:43 P.M.
2. 11:13 A.M.
3. 50 minutes
4. 24 hours and 50 minutes
5. Daylight times for low tide are shown on the chart. Students' reasons will vary.
6. Students' responses will vary. Accept all reasonable responses.

Page 30

Students' responses will vary. Possible responses are listed below.

Person vs. Nature

1. Brian is in conflict with the porcupine that enters his cave.
2. Brian is in conflict with the tornado that destroys his camp.
3. Brian is in conflict with the mosquitoes that swarm all over him.
4. Brian is in conflict with the moose that attacks him.

Person vs. Self

1. Brian is in conflict with himself about whether to tell his dad the Secret.
2. Brian is in conflict with himself about learning to survive.
3. Brian is in conflict with himself about being patient.

Person vs. Person

1. Brian is in conflict with his mother over her leaving his father.
2. Brian is in conflict with the pilot over the pilot's "failure" to reach safety.

Page 36

Students' page numbers will vary depending on the book version but should be located in the chapters listed below.
Ghalas-at—chapter 2
Wild dogs' cave—chapter 8
Black Cave—chapter 20
Karana's house—chapter 11
Freshwater springs—chapter 2
Coral Cove—chapter 2
Sleeping rock—chapter 9
Aleuts' campsite—chapter 2
Headland and cave—chapter 16
Sea elephants' home—chapter 11
Students' maps will vary but should include the listed sites.

Page 38
Part I

	Scientist	Root and Meaning	Focus of Study
	biologist	*bio:* life	the study of life
1.	anthropologist	*anthrop:* human being	the study of the origin, development, and culture of humans
2.	archaeologist	*archae:* primitive, ancient	the study of the remains of a past human culture
3.	ichthyologist	*ichthy:* fish	the study of fishes
4.	entomologist	*entom:* insect	the study of insects
5.	geologist	*ge:* earth	the study of the origin, history, and structure of the earth
6.	herpetologist	*herpet:* reptile	the study of reptiles and amphibians
7.	toxicologist	*toxic:* poison	the study of poisons
8.	marine biologist	*mar:* sea *bio:* life	of or relating to the sea the study of organisms
9.	oologist	*oo:* egg	the study of eggs
10.	seismologist	*seismo:* shock, earthquake	the study of earthquakes

Part II

Students' invitations will vary but should include the reason each scientist would want to visit the Island of the Blue Dolphins.

Page 42

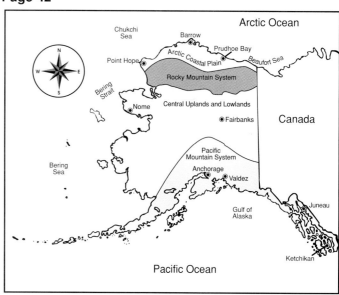

Page 43

Students' responses for the "Your City, State" and "Difference" columns will vary. Responses for the "Barrow, Alaska" column are listed below.

Barrow, Alaska

Average January high	–9°F
Average January low	–22°F
Average July high	46°F
Average July low	33°F
Days of rain or snow in January	4
Days of rain or snow in July	8
Latitude	about 71.30°N
Altitude	about 29' above sea level
Climate Group	tundra

Answer Keys

Page 48
1. lure
2. cache
3. venison
4. avalanche
5. tuber
6. chew
7. mountains
8. chute
9. talons
10. ponder
11. plunge
12. warden
13. gorge
14. bough
15. steep

Page 49
Vitamin E is needed to maintain cell membranes. Sources include whole grains, wheat germ, seed oils, and vegetable oils.

Vitamin A is needed to maintain many body parts, including skin, eyes, bones, teeth, and the lining of the digestive, respiratory, and nervous systems. Sources include eggs, fish liver oil, liver, milk, butter, dark green leafy vegetables, sweet potatoes, carrots, and deep yellow fruits and vegetables.

Vitamin B$_1$ is needed to help the heart and nervous system function properly. It is also required to metabolize carbohydrates. Sources include whole grains, enriched breads, yeast, legumes, nuts, most vegetables, and pork.

Vitamin B$_2$ is needed for healthy skin. It also helps cells use oxygen and promotes the repair of tissues. Sources include poultry, liver, fish, milk, cheese, and green vegetables.

Vitamin B$_6$ is needed to metabolize protein, carbohydrates, and fat. Sources include poultry, organ meats, fish, eggs, nuts, and whole grains.

Vitamin B$_{12}$ is needed to develop red blood cells and to maintain the function of the nervous system. Sources include poultry, fish, meat, milk, and eggs.

Folic acid is needed for the production of red blood cells. Sources include liver, green leafy vegetables, legumes, and fruit.

Vitamin C is needed to maintain healthy bones and teeth and to promote the healing of wounds. Sources include citrus fruits, cantaloupe, strawberries, tomatoes, potatoes, and raw cabbage.

Page 53
cotton gin
1793
Eli Whitney
United States
separates the cottonseeds from the cotton fibers
The cotton gin has a turning cylinder that is studded with wire hooks. The wire hooks push the cotton fibers through narrow slits, which trap the seeds.

threshing machine
1788
Andrew Meikle
Scotland
separates the kernels of grain from the stalks
The threshing machine is powered by horses. It has a turning cylinder that knocks the kernels from the straw. The kernels fall into a bucket, and a conveyor belt carries the straw away.

sulky plow
1875
John Deere
United States
allows the farmer to sit and ride while tilling
The sulky plow is pulled by horses. It has a seat and wheels so the farmer can ride while tilling the land.

reaping machine
1831
Cyrus Hall McCormick
United States
harvests grain faster than farmers with hand tools
The reaping machine is pulled by horses. Its revolving wheel moves a sharp blade that cuts through stalks of grain.

Page 55
Sled and sled dog equipment value = $1,224.00
Survival supplies value = $156.40
Musher equipment value = $679.00
Miscellaneous value = $350.00
Total investment = $2,410.00

Page 59
1. dock
2. pilothouse
3. deck
4. cleat
5. mast
6. starboard
7. cabin
8. rigging
9. skiff
10. tiller
11. outboard
12. oars
13. towline

dinghy: a small boat
hull: the frame or body of a boat
oarlock: a U-shaped device that holds an oar in place
scuppers: openings in a boat that allow water falling on deck to flow overboard
galley: the kitchen on a boat
keel: the chief structure of a boat that extends down the center of its bottom and often projects from the bottom

Page 60
Students' maps should include the locations shown below and ten additional landmarks of students' choosing.

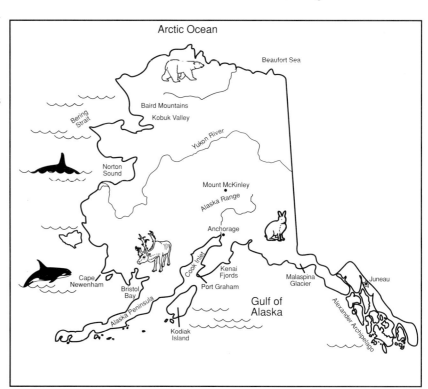